THE ELIXIRS *OF* NOSTRADAMUS

THE ELIXIRS *OF* NOSTRADAMUS

NOSTRADAMUS' ORIGINAL

RECIPES *FOR* ELIXIRS,

SCENTED WATER, BEAUTY

POTIONS *AND* SWEETMEATS

EDITED *BY* KNUT BOESER

MOYER BELL

Wakefield, Rhode Island & London

Published by Moyer Bell
This Edition 1996

First published in Germany by
Rowohlt Taschenbuch Verlag GmbH in 1994

Copyright © 1994 by
Rowohlt Taschenbuch Verlag GmbH, Reinbeck near Hamburg

Text translation by Carola Friedrichs–Friedlander
Translation for Byword by Guy Slatter

Published by arrangement with Bloomsbury Publishing Plc

**LIBRARY OF CONGRESS
CATALOGING IN PUBLICATION DATA**

Nostradamus   The Elixirs of Nostradamus

1. Medicine, Medieval   2. Elixirs   3. Natural cosmetics
   I. Boeser, Knut.

R128.E45   1996   95-348
615'.321'0902--dc20   CIP

ISBN 1-55921-155-5 (cloth)

Printed in Italy

Distributed in North America by Publishers Group West, P.O. Box 8843, Emeryville
CA 94662, 800-788-3123 (in California 510-658-3453) and in Europe by Gazelle
Book Services Ltd., Falcon House, Queen Square, Lancaster LA1 1RN England.

CONTENTS
of this little book

470 307.

NYMPHAEA CANDIDA. vueifseeblumen.

FOREWORD
by Knut Boeser

The two books by Nostradamus that make up this edition were originally published in French in 1552 and subsequently appeared in Augsburg in 1572, in a translation by Dr Hieremias Martius. Only very few copies are still in existence. In this present, unabridged edition of Martius' translation, the text has been carefully modernized to make it more readable. The original is in the Austrian National Library in Vienna. The illustrations in this volume are taken from a Leonhard Fuchs manuscript which is housed in the manuscript department of the Austrian National Library in Vienna (Cat. nos. 11117–25).

Leonhard Fuchs was born in 1501 in Wemding in the Nördlinger Ries, where his father was mayor. Although his father died when Leonhard was five years old, his mother provided him with an excellent education. He first attended schools in Heilbronn and later in Erfurt. At the age of twelve, he went to the university at Erfurt to study for the degree of Bachelor of Arts. At the age of sixteen he opened a school in his home town, but two years later went to Ingolstadt to further his studies in classical languages, studying under the famous humanist Reuchlin, among others. At the age of twenty Fuchs obtained his Master's degree and in 1524 he graduated as a Doctor of Medicine. At an early age he was attracted by the medical writings of Greek authors and the works of Luther. For two years he practised as a doctor in Munich and then returned to Ingolstadt, where, at the age of twenty-four, he became Professor of Medicine. As a Protestant, however, he was not able to remain in the town for long. First he became personal physician to the Protestant Margrave of Brandenburg in Ansbach and then in 1535 he took up a post in Tübingen. He played a major part in the reorganization of the university there and was elected rector seven times. He died in Tübingen in 1566.

Fuchs published more than forty books, principally translations of and commentaries on Greek authors, such as the works of Hippocrates and Galen. His most important book is *De Historia Stirpium Commentarii*, which was published by Michael Isingrin in Basle in 1542. It is a folio volume of 900 pages, illustrated with 511 woodcuts, which even today is regarded as one of the most beautiful herbals. The following year it appeared in German with the title *New Kreuterbuch* . . . (*New Herbal*), 'in which not only the whole history, that is the name, form, place and time of growth, nature, potency and usefulness of the majority of herbs growing in Germany and other countries, is described with great diligence, but also the roots, stems, leaves, flowers, seeds and fruits of the same, in short the whole form is thus described and portrayed in such a skilful and artistic manner, the like of which has never before seen the light of day'. Each plant's description has seven headings: *Nomina* (name), *genera* (characteristics), *forma* (form), *locus* ('place where it grows'), *tempus* (time), *temperamentum* ('nature and complexion') and *vires* ('potency and usefulness'). The illustrations were drawn by the painters Füllmaurer and Meyer, working under Fuchs's direction – many people assert that Holbein also had a hand in the work. Later they were carved in wood by Speckle.

Fuchs intended to follow up his work with two further volumes containing 1,500 illustrations. He was, however, unable to find a publisher for the project, since the first book had not sold well as its cost was so high. He nevertheless finished the manuscript, which was not heard of again for over 200 years, until it was located in 1954 in the Austrian National Library. It consists of nine thick folio volumes with 1,525 magnificent coloured illustrations, among which may be found most of the originals used for the 511 woodcuts in the *De Historia stirpium commentarii*.

Three scholars stand out as the principal founders of modern botany: Otto Brunfels, Hieronymus Bock and Leonhard Fuchs. The first volume of the *Contrafayt Kreuterbuch* (*Illustrated Herbal*) – the German translation of Otto Brunfels's *Herbarum Vivae Eicones* – appeared in 1532 and the second volume in 1537. Brunfels was born in Mainz in 1488. He began by studying theology, converted to Protestantism and found employment with Franz von Sickingen in Kreuznach. Then, thanks to the mediation of Hutten, he became pastor at Steinheim bei Hanau. Later he went to Strasbourg, where he qualified as Doctor of Medicine. He became a professor in Berne and died there in 1534 at the age of forty-six.

Hieronymus Bock's herbal – he called himself Tragus in Latin – appeared in Strasbourg in 1539 under the title of *New Kreütterbuch* . . . (*New Herbal*, 'of the differences, uses and names of the herbs growing in German-speaking lands'). The second edition, published in 1546, contains 465 woodcuts, which are, however, often copies of illustrations appearing in the books of Brunfels and Fuchs. Bock was born in 1498 in Heidelsheim and began by studying theology and then medicine. In 1532 he became preacher at Norbach near Zweibrücken and also received permission to practise there as a doctor. He died in Hornbach in 1554.

A new epoch in work on natural history began with these three botanists, for their interest was of a scientific rather than a religious nature. The plants described by the three authors were carefully observed by them. The illustrations always show the whole plant and are drawn from nature, which at the time was by no means standard practice. Previously descriptions of plants contained all kinds of superstitious speculations, especially ones drawn from Arabic symbolism. What was important was not what one actually saw, but much rather what one believed one knew. Brunfels, Bock and, the most important of the three, Leonhard Fuchs, followed the example of ancient Greek scholars and described exactly what they had found by close observation.

At this point I should like to offer my sincere thanks to the head of the manuscript department of the Austrian National Library in Vienna, Dr Gamillschek, to his colleagues and the National Library for their friendly support and for permission to reproduce some of the magnificent illustrations in this book. In addition, I should like to take this opportunity to thank in particular Mrs Heidemarie Gletthofer, M.A., and Dr Carola Friedrichs-Friedländer. Mrs Gletthofer was of considerable help with research on the texts and illustrations, and then with the selection and arrangement of the pictures. Mrs Friedrichs-Friedländer sympathetically and carefully transcribed Nostradamus' text into modern German, and endeavoured to preserve the unique charm of his descriptions in a manner comprehensible to a modern reader. Finally, thanks are due to Bloomsbury, the British publishers, and Rowohlt, the German publishers, and in particular Dr Siv Bublitz, who have made it possible with this publication for the general public to have access to the words of Nostradamus – a man about whom so much has already been written but whom most people know only by repute – and to see at least a part of Leonhard Fuchs's work.

Knut Boeser, D.Phil., was born in 1944. He studied literary science and philosophy in Berlin and Paris and then lived in Berlin and Vienna, working as a freelance writer. He next became chief dramatist and subsequently stage manager at the Renaissance-Theater in Berlin, and then chief dramatist at the Staalichen Schauspielbühnen in Berlin. He has edited books on Max Reinhardt, Erwin

Piscator and Oskar Panizza. He now lives as a freelance writer in Berlin and Traunkirchen. He wrote the novel *Nostradamus* (rororo 13609), as well as the script for the film of the same name.

119.

ADAMI POMA.   Adams opffel

V.

INTRODUCTION
by Wulfing von Rohr

The most successful plague doctor and most popular miracle healer of his time, sensational prophet of future events and favourite astrologer of the French royal family, much-travelled apothecary of natural medicines and initiated alchemist: those words give an apt description in miniature of that enigmatic and mysterious Doctor of Medicine, who was at the height of his fame in the southern French town of Salon-de-Provence from 1547 until his death in 1566.

In this work we propose to concentrate primarily on the subjects of medicine, herbal medicine and alchemy, which played such an important role in Nostradamus' life, and leave his comprehensive prophetic work of almost 1,000 portentous verses to other publications.

Michel de Notredame, at times also written Nostredame, first saw the light of day as the clock was striking noon on 14 December 1503, according to the Julian calendar, in the small locality of Saint-Rémy-de-Provence in southern France.

At the time of his birth who could have told him that one day, under his Latinized name of Nostradamus, he would go down in the annals of world history as 'Plague healer of Provence', 'Doctor of France', 'The Initiated One' and 'Greatest Seer of the Renaissance'? Who could have foretold that this son of a middle-class former Jewish family which had been compelled to convert to Catholicism would become one of the most famous Frenchmen of the sixteenth century? Did he himself know, or at least suspect, that his works and writings would survive for hundreds of years and be numbered among the most widely read books after the Bible?

There is no disagreement among those doing research

about Nostradamus that he came from Jewish stock on both his father's and his mother's side; many commentaries even maintain that he came from the tribe of Issachar, famed for its prophetic powers. First Michel's parents – father Jacques, a notary, and mother Renée – complied with Louis XII's edict of September 1501 and later on had their three children, Michel, Bertrand and Jean, baptized.

On the other hand, there is some dispute as to whether the grandparents were doctors who for a time worked in the service of the Count of Provence, or made their living as successful corn-merchants.

During the course of many long years Michel grew up in the home of his grandfather Jean, who was able to pass on to him a wide-ranging education. Michel learned mathematics, Latin, Greek and Hebrew and was initiated into the first stages of astrology.

At that time astrology was regarded as one of the diagnostic aids and one of the therapeutically significant temporal guides for medicine – as indeed is once again the case in many places today. The horoscope was studied in order to find reasons for illnesses and to ascertain the most suitable times for mixing certain medicines. From our own modern hospitals we know that an unusually large number of complications with operations, unpleasant post-operative bleeding and general psychic difficulties still arise during full or new moons. In the Renaissance astrology played a very significant role in medicine; medicine, alchemy and astrology were regarded as kindred sciences.

Michel was sent to Avignon to complete a kind of '*studium generale*'. During his lifetime Avignon had changed from being a papal seat to a centre of 'modern' education. Michel is said to have devoted himself mainly to the study of the movements of and laws governing the heavenly firmament. That is why he is said to have had the nickname 'the small astrologer'.

Michel's father was concerned about his eldest son's interests, which even at that time were apparently considered of 'little practical use', and at the age of sixteen he sent him to the highly regarded Montpellier University to study medicine and embark on a career as a doctor, thereby acquiring a solid foundation for later life.

At the age of nineteen, in 1522, Michel gained his Bachelor's degree at Montpellier. For three years he had studied classical medicine and attended lectures by the most famous doctors in Europe. He was entitled to exchange the students' black robe for the red one of a qualified man.

After three further years Michel had probably learned all that was known at that time about medicine and obtained his certification as a practising doctor from the Bishop of Montpellier.

In the south of France in the same year there were once again sporadic outbreaks of the plague, that most terrifying epidemic of the period. In the Middle Ages the plague reduced the total population of Europe by a third. With good reason people felt they were helpless in the face of a sickness which affected both rich and poor, young and old, sick and healthy without distinction and carried them off in a swift and most painful manner.

Michel interrupted his studies – he was still seeking to obtain a doctorate – left the university and began to put his newly acquired and, indeed, officially recognized knowledge into practice. In Montpellier and the surrounding area the young man laid the foundation of his subsequent reputation as a plague doctor and the author of miraculous cures. He cured more victims of the plague than any other doctor.

Historians, medical men and biographers attribute his success primarily to two reasons: Michel possessed an unusual degree of self-confidence and indomitable courage, which enabled him to visit the houses of plague victims. In addition, he prepared his own medicaments, which were wonderfully effective, either medicinally or psychologically.

Michel visited patients in the surrounding countryside and eventually travelled to Narbonne. There he attended lectures and meetings of well-known Jewish alchemists. At that time there was a very close connection between alchemy and pharmacology, the preparation of magical potions and the creations of the apothecary. Michel travelled and practised in Carcassonne, where, among other things, he wished to be in the service of Bishop Amenien de Fays. For him he prescribed an 'elixir of life' in the form of a pomade, the recipe for which is contained in the book, entitled: '*Excellent et moult utile Opuscule a tout necessaire qui desirent auoir cognoissance de plusieurs exquises Recepts, divise en deux parties . . .*' This is the original French version of the present text, which was printed in Lyons in 1552 at the press of Antoine Volant.

The next places he visited were Toulouse, Bordeaux and, finally, Avignon. The papal legate there, Cardinal Clermont, Grand Master of the Knights of St John (who had called themselves Knights of Malta since 1522), was presented by him with a 'quince jelly of regal beauty, goodness, taste and excellence'.

Michel irrefutably cured the most serious illnesses of the time in such an astonishing number of cases that he soon acquired the reputation of being able to work miracles. During these years of teaching and moving from place to place he was, however, already producing tinctures which were supposed to aid rejuvenation and virility and, hopefully, the attainment of 'eternal youth'. He also knew how to please members of the aristocracy with recipes for unusual delicacies.

In 1529 he returned to Montpellier, where the plague epidemic had abated. During the examination for his doctorate he was asked to justify the value of his unorthodox medicines. He passed with flying colours and received the coveted title of Doctor of Medicine, the characteristic four-pointed hat, a golden ring and a copy of Hippocrates' book. From then on he called himself 'Nostradamus' – even in those days a Latin-sounding name did not fail to inspire respect. Nostradamus accepted an invitation to fill a teaching post in the faculty of medicine. He did not, however, feel constrained for long to follow the old teaching methods, the practical virtue of which he doubted. Thus, for example, Nostradamus spoke out against the habit of bleeding each and every patient (and thereby unnecessarily weakening them), no matter what illness had been diagnosed.

In 1530 the great French poet (and mystic) Rabelais received his doctorate in Montpellier. Most of Nostradamus' biographers cannot agree on whether there was direct contact between him and Rabelais; however, Manfred Dimde, the most important German Nostradamus expert, considers that he can prove close co-operation in the realms of medicine and magic and in the constitution of a secret society.

In 1532 Nostradamus packed up his books and instruments, saddled his mule and for two years wandered as a 'mounted physician' through the countryside of southern France. During his wanderings an invitation reached him from the small town of Agen. It came from one of the leading men in Europe, the highly esteemed Jules César Scaliger, who was considered to be almost the equal of Erasmus of Rotterdam. Nostradamus settled in Agen, worked together with the learned Scaliger, carried on a lucrative pratice and married a 'well-born, very beautiful and lovely' young woman who bore him a son and daughter. Strangely enough, the names of these three are not recorded anywhere, yet there is no doubt of their existence.

After three idyllic years Nostradamus was hit by one misfortune after another. His wife and children died; it is not certain whether this was as a result of the 'black death' or diphtheria. Patients began to stay away. Who can trust a doctor who cannot cure his own family? Scaliger, who is said to have been a particularly contentious and incomprehensible person, and Nostradamus had such a quarrel that their friendship came to an end. Manfred Dimde suggests that, following the premature death of his wife, Nostradamus may have had to give back part of her dowry, which placed him in financial difficulties. Finally, the Inquisition is said to have been interested in him; and the Protestant Calvin was staying in the neighbourhood for a long time and many people began to speak evil of Nostradamus. In 1538 he was summoned by the Church authorities to appear before the Inquisitor of Toulouse.

Nostradamus left Agen and spent the years from 1538 to 1544 on the move. He travelled northwards as far as Lorraine, eastwards to Venice and to Sicily in the south. No doubt he helped and cured people wherever he was needed, earning his keep in this manner. At the same time, however, he increased his knowledge through numerous meetings and working together with alchemists, astrologers, sorcerers and members of secret societies.

In 1544 Nostradamus stopped for some time in Marseilles in order to help bring a fresh outbreak of the plague under control. In 1546 the black death gained a hold in the province's main city, Aix-en-Provence. Nostradamus was summoned and devoted himself courageously and in a determined manner to the healing of the sick and above all to preventive measures among the healthy. He spent days, weeks and months in the midst of the appalling atmosphere of wholesale death and despair and was indeed able to cure people and to sow seeds of fresh hope.

His remedies included 'rose pills', which were to be made as follows:

one ounce of sawdust from the greenest available cypress
  tree
six ounces of Florentine iris
three ounces of cloves
three drachms of sweet flag (root)
six drachms of resinous aloe wood

These ingredients are pulverized and then 300 to 400 red
roses, which have been picked before the grey light of dawn
and similarly pulverized, are mixed in with them. Throughout
care is taken to prevent undue exposure to the air. The mixture
is then shaped into pills, which the patient constantly keeps in
the mouth. According to Michel, the wonderful scent can kill
bad breath and foul smells and clean rotten teeth.

Nostradamus was of the opinion that the plague was spread
by contaminated air, and that clean air protected the patients.
Perhaps his success lay simply in the fact that fleas, which are
known to transmit the plague from rats to humans, could not
stand the mixture's strong smell and thus at least the healthy
were stopped from catching the disease.

Whatever the reason, his reputation and his prestige as a
plague healer grew.

Salon was the next town to lay claim to his medical skills.
Here, too, Nostradamus was successful. He liked Salon so
much that he settled there and continued to live in the
town right up to the end of his life. A short stay in Lyons,
in order to combat the plague there as well, brought him
further successes, honour and a very good income. In 1547
Nostradamus married Anne Ponsard Gemelle, a rich widow
of Salon.

In Salon Nostradamus had finally found the right atmosphere to allow him to carry on secret studies and alchemical
experiments, to make astrological observations and calcula-
tions as well as to ponder on prophetic visions. His medical

practice was not particularly exciting and he seems to have spent most of his time working on recipes for special cosmetic preparations for members of the nobility in the surrounding district.

Tracité des Fardemens, the first of his non-prophetic books, appeared in 1552. This was followed by a whole series of books and writings in which he set down a multitude of instructions for making medicinally effective preparations and recipes for all kinds of cosmetics, for elixirs of youth and even for the proper way to make jams and jellies. Incidentally, these themes also crop up in the 'yearly almanacs', the prophetic calendars which he published.

The first part of his *Centurien* appeared in 1555. This was the great prophetical work, composed in quatrains, on the history of the world from 1555 to 3797.

A prophet who already enjoyed an unusual reputation as a plague doctor, miraculous healer and magician – today he would be described as an 'esoteric man' – not only over a wide area of Provence but beyond the borders of France as well, such a man aroused the imagination of more than just the 'common' folk. Nostradamus became a topic of conversation among the upper classes and his reputation as a soothsayer reached the court.

On 14 July 1556 Nostradamus set out on the then very difficult journey from Salon to the French court in Paris. In spite of having permission to use the royal post coach, the journey lasted a full month. Queen Catherine de Medici, who was particularly interested in prophecy and the supernatural, had invited him to demonstrate his knowledge and skill to the royal couple and courtiers to the best of his ability.

His visit to the area was a great success. Nostradamus knew how to impress the king and queen through prophecies (subsequently disputed) about themselves. He was able to acquire clients from among members of the aristocracy and the prosperous middle class. He shone as a prophet and astrologer, as well as through his medical skill and the prescribing of arbitrary, yet evidently effective, aids to virility and cosmetic powders and ointments which, at least in the eyes of the ladies, obviously fully fulfilled their purpose.

As a result Nostradamus was visited in Salon year in, year out by members of the aristocracy and the nobility. For a time he was appointed court doctor (residing far from Paris); he enjoyed the reputation of a prophet and medical man recognized by the court. Nostradamus had reached the high point of his life.

Michel de Nostredame, called Nostradamus, died on 2 July 1566, according to the calendar of that time. As far as posterity is concerned he is, without doubt, best remembered for his prophetic visions. Among his contemporaries, however, at least in the first two-thirds of his life, Nostradamus was famous for his extraordinary medical and alchemical skills.

The fact that his original recipes are now being made available to a wider public is one step towards once again portraying Nostradamus for what he was: an open-minded doctor and sympathetic healer, with intense feeling for the forces of nature, and a preserver of mysterious recipes, handed down through the ages.

Wulfing von Rohr is a television journalist and writer. He is the co-author of ten books on natural healing, including *Die richtige Schwingung heilt* and *Die Farben deiner Seele*. He has done considerable research on Nostradamus and published his findings in an authoratative book, *Nostradamus – Seher und Astrologe entschlüsselte Geheimnisse und ungelöste Rätsel*. His latest book is entitled *Es steht geschrieben . . . ist unser Leben Zufall oder Schicksal – von Palmblattbibliotheken und heiligen Schriften*.

❧ TWO BOOKS *by the renowned and highly learned philosopher, astrologer and physician, Michel Nostradamus.*

In which a true, thorough and complete account is given as to how a disfigured body, be it of man or woman, may be externally embellished, beautified and rejuvenated as well as the correct and proper methods of preparing all kinds of aromatic, precious and potent lotions, powders, oils, soaps, perfumed candles and musk balls for use against all kinds of infirmities. And how, in the second part, all kinds of fruits may be preserved in sugar in the most skilful and delectable manner and stored against a time of need. Originally written by him in the French language: now, however, for the benefit of our fatherland, it has been translated into ordinary German in the most excellent manner by Hieremias Martius, appointed Doctor of Medicine at Augsburg.

Not to be reprinted – by order of His Imperial Roman Majesty.
MDLXXII

❧ TO THE MOST SERENE HIGHNESS

*Right Honourable Princess and Lady, Lady
Christina, former Queen of Denmark, Sweden
and Norway and Duchess of Milan, Lorraine
and Barr and Widow, my most gracious Princess
and Lady.*

*Most Serene Highness, Right Honourable Princess, Most gracious
Lady, be assured, Your Royal Highness, of my most unworthy,
obedient and humble service. That most excellent and heartfelt praise
has been the copious reward throughout the ages of those who have,
either from their own superior intellect, themselves made some useful
discovery or have, to the best of their ability, increased and improved
upon something discovered by others, may easily be seen from history
books and old tales and more besides. From these it appears that such
persons are not only rewarded by grateful people with expensive and
valuable gifts but, what is much more to be wondered at, are even
taken for gods and divine reverence is afforded them. This fact has
been no small stimulus to their descendants, particularly those whom
Almighty God has endowed with a greater degree of wisdom and
understanding to reflect upon things in a somewhat more industrious,
serious and zealous manner and to bring to light that which has so far
remained hidden. For this reason in our forefathers' days, and still
today, large and significant sums of money have been spent upon the
upkeep of worthy persons, whose names have subsequently become
immortal, whereby they have attained and received everlasting fame
and praise. Examples may from time to time be found in history books
by a man who only reads such works and concentrates carefully upon
them. Thus, in a similar manner to other such people, Aesculapius
was revered by the heathen as a god. Likewise the ancient, highly
renowned and learned Hippocrates was received with exceptional*

reverence by his countrymen and his beloved fatherland and was accorded great honour, because he had brought the healing art of medicine back from darkness to light. Directly excluded from consideration, however, must be all those who have either thought up some evil from their own wantonness or inquisitiveness or have discovered something which may in part harm other people and in part may lead them themselves to extreme ruin. And, just as such people are properly hated by many and shunned by everyone wherever possible, so those who have discovered something divine, useful and wholesome from a Christ-like disposition, unstinted diligence and innate love towards their neighbour, whom they heartily desire to serve, are rightly held in high esteem and preferred before the others, who follow idleness and lust rather than the liberal arts.

Therefore it is right that Michel Nostradamus, the illustrious philosopher, astrologer and physician, who in a miraculous way progressed beyond all the things necessary for a man to know, should be highly praised and be most worthy of an immortal name on account of his superior intellect because during his lifetime, which lasted many years, he spared neither diligence nor effort in the service of other people and was able to help in many ways. To this end he therefore wished to experience all kinds of things and so personally undertook long and difficult journeys, so that he could learn something from others. He travelled throughout a good part of the world and thereby obtained such a knowledge of many strange and secret things, which he would not otherwise have learned unless he were Apollo himself, for whom nothing would have remained unknown. Together with other credible persons I can bear ample witness to this. For when, in the Year of Our Lord 1558, he was walking through Montpellier, a well-known town in Languedoc, with the firm intention of riding off in great haste, he was detained for several days against his will by a number of sick persons, who were anxious to ask his advice and also speak to him about other matters, in spite of the fact that the aforementioned place was exceptionally well provided with the leading and most learned doctors in the whole of Christendom. In the end the crowd became so great that he had to shut himself up in a special apartment. What he prophesied about King Francis, the first of this name of most praiseworthy memory, before he set off towards Pavia, was amply borne out by the pitiful outcome of the expedition and the dismal dungeon. How, too, a long time beforehand, he foresaw the recent terrible and almost unbelievable overthrow of the Turks and the glorious victory of the Christians, albeit in an allegorical and obscure manner, as was his custom, and how few things, which are just coming to pass, were unknown to or hidden from him.

No further proof is necessary of the fact that he was an excellent and distinguished doctor, since he earnestly and with great diligence devoted almost the whole of his life to questions relating to this healing and useful art. It is impossible to assess the extent of the benefits which he brought to the sick during the course of so many years. How many people he seized from the jaws of death, so to speak, and freed from terrifying disease and, like another Hippocrates, stopped the pestilence and drove it off. How chivalrously he behaved. How courageously he counteracted and opposed the horrible and previously unheard-of pestilence at Aix, a place within the province, in the Year of Our Lord 1548. He did the same in Lyons in the Year of Our Saviour 1547, as you will find adequately reported elsewhere in this small book. I will not dwell on the fact that in his dealings with other people he was invariably friendly and charming and was always glad to be of service and, as a proof and practical demonstration of this, in the Year of Our Lord 1552 he had this present small book printed. It was written at the request of and as a most humble offering to a great princess and imparted by him to his best and most intimate friends as a precious jewel and hidden treasure. There can be no doubt that it is indeed his work, for anyone who has once read his works will easily conclude that this is his style because, as far as this matter is concerned, there is something which differentiates it from others. Therefore, when I read this through carefully and found so much in it that would make it worth the effort of translating into our German language as a highly useful source of material, I immediately, in the name of God (certain doubting Thomases may say what they like), began to translate the work into German in the most accurate, clear and comprehensible manner possible, paying more attention to the sense and content of each item than the mere words. I will not go into details here of the effort this entailed – should anyone else do the same, he will know what it means.

This work of his, however, is divided into two distinct books, which are totally dissimilar, for in the first book are clearly shown the ways and means by which a person may remain beautiful and youthful for a long while, and everything is included which appertains to external adornment and well-being. In the other, however, only those things are included which are to be used internally, either for pleasure or to provide energy and strength for the sick and weak, namely how all kinds of fruits are to be preserved in sugar in the best possible manner, a skill which is not possessed by everyone. Many may deceive themselves that they are able to do this, but they do not yet know the definitive method and I can truthfully say that I have never seen the like in my lifetime. Yes, he is the first to have written these things down in an orderly manner, for which we owe him a just debt of gratitude. At this point, however, I must answer those who might raise objections and say that it would be a waste of time to prescribe things in it for women, since many of them spend all day and night thinking about how they can actually remain beautiful and it is not good for them to desire more than that with which nature has endowed them. I answer such people as follows: a woman's true adornment is either seen internally in her nature, that is to say in her good virtues, or externally in her complexion or the beauty of her body. The eyes are likewise attractive beyond measure: if a body is well formed or the hair of a member of the fairer sex is blonde and her eyes dark – such attributes are special gifts. If, however, nature has formed someone in an uncomely fashion, I question whether we should not be allowed to attempt to remove this deficiency with the artifice which is always ascribed to nature. Similarly, if one takes *particular pleasure in good manners, is charmed by shapely people and finally delights in natural beauty, how much more should one be inspired by those who have only become so through artificial means, for it is very easy to do so where nature also endows a person with a fine intellect, but exceptionally difficult to instil the latter where it does not exist beforehand. Thus one frequently encounters people who, although their face may be beautiful, are, however, very hairy. Likewise others have a beautiful red mouth and lips, but black teeth and foul breath. Should not these people be allowed to address such imperfections at an early stage and seek advice, for when one is young one seeks to preserve everything which seems beautiful in the eyes of another. Then, when the person becomes old, he or she will at least have beautiful children. Indeed, wherever there is merely a single mole or spot on the body, a person will seek out all kinds of ways and means of getting rid of it or at least keeping it concealed. Should, however, someone say that the members of the fairer sex have up until now not been satisfied with all this, but have continued to think up new concoctions and lotions, making themselves ugly in the process, to such a person I would reply that that happens in all kinds of things and is not confined to the matter in hand. For it does not follow that because some people misuse these artifices they are, therefore, to be condemned. Just because iron can kill a man, fire burn him or food sometimes choke him, it does not, therefore, mean that one should cease to use them, for no matter how beautiful a member of the fairer sex may be, by using the right skills one can produce such an effect that she appears even more beautiful, while bearing in mind that nothing in this world is truly perfect.*

Since, gracious lady, it is an ancient, praiseworthy and long-established custom that when someone either writes something for the general good or interprets the work of other people or transfers it into another language and prepares it for publication, such a person must seek and look out for a patron, after much deliberation and careful consideration my thoughts, for many noble and good reasons, turned first to you, Your Royal Highness, to whom I ascribe and dedicate this small book and under whose shield and protection and mighty name I have had the same printed. In the first place, as far as I know and have been able to find out from your courtiers, while he was still alive Your Royal Highness looked with favour upon him and honoured him with an annuity from the state. What also gave me no slight encouragement to pursue my intentions was the confident knowledge that Your Royal Highness would graciously take pleasure in this my work, on account of the sympathetic manner in which it treats the blessed memory of Nostradamus and serves to further the spread of his fame and good reputation and will accept it with fond memories and as a precious jewel and pearl of great price. A further reason is the fact that this small book deals with matters which appertain only to great lords and ladies. Thus, through the blessing of the Almighty, I have been able to apply to them to offset the expenses and it has, therefore, been much easier for me to write to you, Your Royal Highness. The third and final reason is because I have heard that Your Royal Highness is particularly well disposed towards the poor, the weak and the sick and is exceptionally endowed with all royal virtues and is most frequently considered to be a highly understanding, kind and gentle princess, and cannot always have the services of honest apothecaries while in the countryside and travels back and forth, so that she may have such refreshing drinks or invigorating syrups and confections prepared for herself at each and every place, I have desired to ascribe it to this lady above all others as though it were her own property, with the most humble request that the said Royal Highness will graciously accept my work, allow it to find favour with her, will protect and defend it against all who would speak evil against it and so help to preserve and honour the good name of the late Nostradamus. I herewith commend you to the protection of the Almighty, that He may graciously preserve Your Royal Family, together with your royal ancestors and most praiseworthy family, in continual good health and may your reign be prosperous and peaceful until you attain the glory and salvation of eternal life.

Given in Augsburg on the twenty-fourth day of February in the

Year of Our Redeemer 1572, on which day the most high and mighty, invincible hero, Charles V, Roman Emperor, was born into this world in the Year of Christ 1500 and, afterwards, on the very same day in the Year of Christ 1530 was crowned at Bologna by Pope Clement, the seventh of that name. On this day, too, in the Year of Our Saviour 1525, Francis, the first of this name, King of France, a Christian, pious and God-fearing prince, was taken prisoner by the renowned Charles V.

Your Royal Highness, by the very hand of your humble and obedient servant, Hierimias Martius, appointed Doctor of Medicine.

BOOK ONE

❦ HOW TO PREPARE THE SUBLIMATE

This sublimate is one of the most excellent lotions in the world for whitening the complexion, for it makes the skin white as snow, without any kind of harmful after-effect. Moreover, it does not cause wrinkles, nor does it harm the teeth in any way, but imparts to the face a sheen which looks as natural as if it had been inborn. Its effect is such that, were a member of the fairer sex with blonde or raven hair to have spots on her face and were she to be as much as fifty-five years old, if she were to use this lotion, her forehead and cheeks would look as if she were just twelve years old. It is indeed such an excellent lotion that even if a man were to come very close to the face, he would not be aware of anything unusual, but would believe it was naturally that white. This is such a wonderful concoction that, if a member of the fairer sex used the lotion for four or five days, her appearance would be such that she would hardly be recognized by her relations or those who previously were her close companions. Furthermore, if a member of the fairer sex were to begin to use this lotion at the age of fifteen, twenty or twenty-five, for the rest of her life her complexion would remain exceptionally beautiful, so that even in her sixtieth year she would have the appearance of being only twenty. It is not difficult to confirm that when this is used over a period of time, it restores the face to health, so that it appears immaculate without any kind of harmful after-effect. It gives it a natural sheen and makes the chin as red as a rose. It will also redden the lips and the cheeks, no matter how pale they may otherwise be, so that, if a young girl or maturer member of the fairer sex were to have a face like death or a sad or melancholy countenance, it will make her appear cheerful and attractive and remove the red patches from her face or soon

113.

CITRIA, MEDI CAVE MALVS OBLON GA OVATAVE

langelechter citronbaum.

II.

drive them away from wherever they may otherwise appear on her body. This, then, is the precious lotion by which many who claimed to be so clever and knowledgeable in being able to recognize natural and unadulterated beauty in a member of the fairer sex have been shamefully deceived and led on and believed they were acquiring Helen, instead of an erstwhile Hecuba. This lotion and the colouring it achieves are so utterly desirable that there are many ladies in Italy, France and Spain who have passed on the knowledge of this skill to their daughters as their most valuable and best dowry. They have not done so in writing, lest others might learn of it, but they have passed it on in secret and instructed them how to mix it together in the most suitable manner, so that it has the potency and ability to colour the face, so that it gleams like silver and, even if it is distinctly copper-coloured, the lotion can make it look thoroughly beautiful and white, so that nature herself, by her natural means, could not achieve a better effect. Similarly, if anyone were to have small blisters or spots on his face, as if it were a kind of leprosy, it would rid him of this unhealthy and obnoxious colour and make it become white. It would make no difference whether the blisters were those left following gangrene or if he had had a limb amputated or been otherwise injured or, indeed, if he had had them from birth, in a short time they would have completely disappeared (although that excellent doctor Hippocrates has written that amputated limbs do not grow again, which is indeed perfectly true and goes without saying). The following preparation, however, has the special property and apparent potency and effect that it is able to achieve what appears impossible. This has been amply borne out by appearances and experienced by many women who have used it and consider it to be the most excellent skill which has ever been acquired.

Take six ounces of mercuric chloride, put it in a clean marble mortar, pound it finely with a wooden pestle and continue doing so, though in a place out of the wind, for almost a whole day, until it is as fine as possible. You will then soon see that it is like finely ground flour and when you take it in your hand you will notice no coarse bits and it will run very gently through your fingers. Now stir in with it the spittle of a young man who, for three days, has neither eaten garlic, nor onions, nor vinegar, nor anything disagreeable and, when you have stirred it for a good while, add pure mercury to it and strain it through a white, thick and well-cleaned woollen cloth. Next take as much as six drachms (or as much as six shining crowns) of lead and tin and three grains of ground silver, mix these ingredients up well together and carry on stirring for a good while, always continuing to add the spittle of a young man. Do this for as long as it takes for the mercury to appear really white, for when the mercury is first mixed with the mercuric chloride it turns black and soon afterwards grey. That is why it is necessary to go on stirring, though not all at one time, until it turns white, because it takes seven days to reach perfection, or its full potential. After the mercury has been well mixed with the spittle and ground to powder, it should be put in a mortar which is made entirely from wood, because neither copper nor iron must be allowed to come into contact with it. Afterwards place it in the sun to dry, since it has to acquire the necessary whiteness from sunshine and hard pounding. Once it has been dried in this manner it should immediately be pounded again. As it is not always possible to obtain spittle, take sea-anemone or rose-water and add it slowly to the mixture. To make the lotion properly, however, you do need genuine spittle and it does not matter if you add to it over a period of several days. As soon as you can see that it is very white and fine, put it out every day in the sun and take care that it binds together well. In the morning stir it briskly at the bottom with a wooden spatula, then dissolve

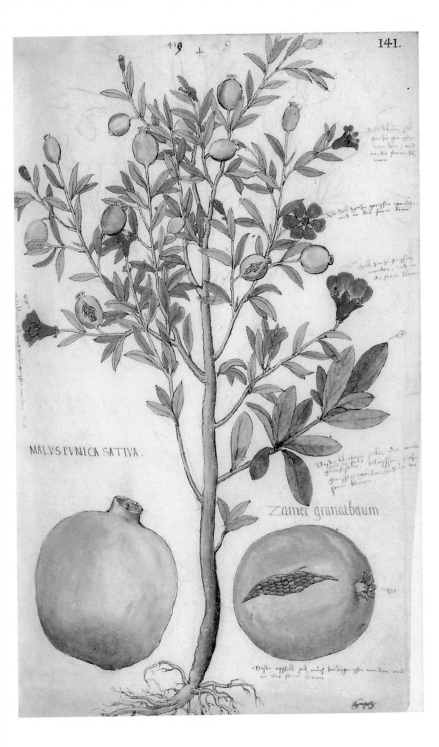

141.

MALVS PVNICA SATIVA.

Zamer granatbaum

it in well water, of which you need about three quarts, or as much as is necessary to liquefy it. Then put it into a small glazed earthenware pot and boil it over a fire, but take care not to let it boil over. Do this for no longer than it takes to say two '*paternosters*' and two '*ave marias*', then take it off the fire and let it cool down. Leave it standing for three or four hours or, to make it all the better, until morning. Then drain off this bitter and poisonous water, which will be green in colour, and give it to the surgeons. Once this has been thoroughly drained off, pour another lot over the mixture and boil it as has already been described. Take it off the fire, let it stand, drain it off and once again replace it with fresh water. Do this six times. Finally, however, use a very aromatic rose-water, let that come to the boil two or three times and do not drain it off, but let it half dry out. When you want to use it, take a piece the size of a pea or half a bean, rub it down with a little rose-water on a marble slab the size of a table-top, moisten a fine and delicate small linen cloth in it and, when you have washed your face thoroughly, apply it the next day to your whole face and it will become exceptionally beautiful and white. Should it, however, become too white, take the root of the true alkanet, together with a small drop of nutmeg oil (how you are to make this will be revealed at the proper time), apply it to the palms of your hands and run them over the lips, cheeks and chin. In order to make the face appear as beautiful as if it had merely been made for gazing upon and so as to ensure that the lotion continues to work and remain effective for a long time, if within a couple of days or so it appears a little black, brown or white like paper, take three ounces of Venetian white lead to a painter, let him grind it with rose-water as finely as possible on a marble slab and, when that has been done, pour three quarts of rose-water, or any other perfumed water, over it, then put it in a large earthenware vessel and warm it a little. Let your hairdresser spend half an hour washing your face, or any other part of your body you may wish, with this mixture and then dry you with a clean sponge, before washing you again with other water. Then, when you have washed with the white lead three days in succession, use the sublimate in the morning when you get up and put your clothes on, but take care not to use too much, for it is sufficient if each time you use an amount the size of a pea and, so that in the long run it does not adversely affect the teeth or harm them, in order to counter this, I always make it with the perfumed water described hereafter.

❦ ANOTHER METHOD *of preparing the sublimate and mixing it properly, so that it is no less effective for cleansing the face than the former.*

The following method of preparing the sublimate, which may be done more quickly than the previous one, is less suitable for making the face pretty and spotless but is exceptionally good for whitening the skin of a person of thirty-five or forty years of age. Even if it does not have exactly the same sheen, it will retain the colour for a longer period. This lotion was used by Lays of Corinth, the most beautiful woman in the whole of Thessalonia. Once it has been on the face for half a quarter of an hour it takes on the appearance of an English complexion and is so extraordinarily white that even those who are experts on the subject of painted or coloured faces are unable to notice or detect anything, so cunning is it and so attractive the result. Once you have tried it three or four times, you will sing its praises far more powerfully and eloquently than I can with my writing. It is, however, much simpler to make than the previous method. It is true that, while this one is worthy of everlasting praise on account of its potency, effect and good qualities, were a member of the fairer sex to use both, she would not despise this one nor consider it to be inferior to the previous one.

This, then, is how to prepare it.

Take four small limes and quarter them. Add to or on to each segment a crown – or good-sized piece of mercury, distil it in a glass phial or, if you are unable to acquire one, take a glass container, chop the segments up as finely as possible and fill the glass not more than half full. Next, place it in a

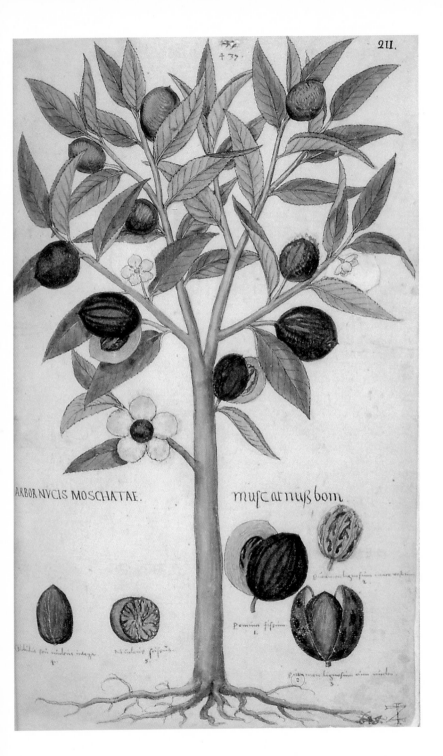

211.

ARBOR NVCIS MOSCHATAE.   muſcat nuſʒ bom

vessel which has been used for burning roses, half bury it in raked or sifted ashes, so that it does not break, and then make a good fire and pour the distilled water drop by drop into another glass container, which you keep separate. Then take four ounces of mercuric chloride, which has not much salt in it, a crown's weight of the best and purest mercury and put them both into a marble mortar, but the pestle and spatula must be of wood. Pulverize it, then take the said water and slowly moisten or sprinkle the mercuric chloride with it for almost a whole day, until it becomes completely white. An even better result can be achieved if you allow it to stand in the sun for several days, for that is very beneficial in such cases. Once it is beautiful and white, grind it to powder using well water, let it come to the boil four times in a freshly glazed earthenware pot and then let it cool down for four hours. Then strain the water and drain it off and pour a second lot over the mixture. Boil that as before, let it cool again and drain it off; do this four times.

Finally, take half a pound of Venetian white lead, make it into a paste with the whites of six eggs, wrap this up in three small white linen cloths, which should be delicate, tie the bundle up and boil it in a new earthenware vessel. When it froths, lift it off with a white quill or silver spoon and, when you have done that, put everything into the glass container with the said water prepared from limes. When the mercuric chloride is saturated, add that to it, taking care that no water remains in the vessel in which it was, mix everything together and when you want to apply it to your face, give the contents of the container a good stir, moisten a woollen cloth or patch in it and wash your face with it in the morning, before you leave your house. For those who now have red, bronzed or leprous faces, it will remove the redness in a few days and make the complexion appear naturally white, for it consumes the bad or impure blood, makes the hair sleek and elegant, without in any way causing injury or harm to other parts of the body, and enlivens the complexion to a state of perfect harmony. Even if a man were to search the whole world, he would not find a lotion to compare with this one.

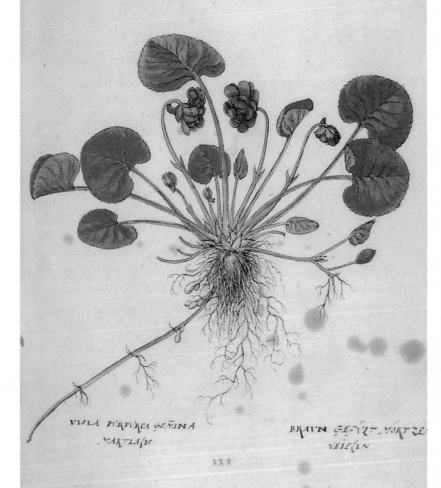

VIOLA PVRPVREA GEMINA
MARTIA 15

BRAVN GEFÜLT VÖRTZEN
VEIELN

111

❧ MAKING PRECIOUS GREEN POMADE

Take about four pounds of lard from a pig which has been slaughtered just the previous day and is very fresh, and place it in a large earthenware pot, together with as much rose-water as is necessary. Knead it thoroughly with clean hands and mix it well together for an hour. Next take twelve of the best-smelling apples that you have or can obtain, chop them up into small pieces without peeling them and likewise chop up the skin or peel of four bitter oranges, two limes and half a lemon, if you are able to find them. Put these chopped-up pieces into a marble mortar and crush everything together as well as you can. When everything is well and truly pounded and thoroughly mixed, add ten ounces of the pulverized roots of Florentine violets, two ounces of well-crushed cloves, two and a half ounces of the aromatic gum of *storax calamita* and an ounce of sweet flag. Pound everything as finely as possible, adding rose-water if there is not enough in the mixture, and put it into an earthenware pot which is well glazed. Let it dissolve over embers or a low fire and cover it with an earthenware dish, but take care that it does not break or crack. If very small cracks do appear, it will not do any serious damage, so stir it thoroughly with a wooden spatula until you are certain that it has completely dissolved. Test it frequently in the following manner: put a drop on your hand and smell it and see whether it has been made properly, for it does not require a lot of boiling. When, however, you feel it is time to remove it from the fire, take about a scruple of musk, though if you want to make the pomade really excellent, add a further drachm to that quantity, so that it weighs about a crown, and then add a drachm and a half of grey amber. Pulverize both, add rose-water, drain it off into a pot, let it boil a bit and then strain everything, while still warm, through a fine, clean cloth into some small glass dishes, each holding three or four ounces, or into a large pot, for it will stay warm and much firmer if you do this. And if you want it to turn completely red, then take three or four roots of the true alkanet, boil them up with what is left over from the whitening process and then it will turn a beautiful scarlet and will be suitable for members of the fairer sex who have a pale complexion, and will be very useful for them. The sediment, however, may be used as an exquisite and very desirable soap for, apart from the desirable and exquisite scent which it gives off, it makes rough hands smooth and soft, if they are rubbed with it frequently.

If, however, you desire to make your pomade something special, excellent and perfect, better than ever before, then, during the season when roses are growing and in bloom, take about 300 or 400 white ones, crush them with the pomade in a marble mortar and, when you have done so, leave the mixture to stand for a day or two. At the end of this period take a similar quantity of white roses, crush them once more, as you have been instructed, and when you have done this, put the whole into a pewter vessel, which is perfectly clean and closes properly. The lid must be carefully sealed with leaven. Now fill a cauldron with water and bring it to the boil and then place the pewter vessel in the middle of the cauldron. The water in the vessel will boil without air or steam, because of the heat. When it has been boiled in this fashion for about two or three hours, take the vessel out of the cauldron, open it and strain the contents through a clean cloth into a glass container. You will then well and truly be able to say that you have the most precious pomade in the world. For indeed no other can compare with it either in scent, potency or effect. It possesses, however, another hidden virtue, which may clearly be seen among those who, against their will, are impotent in the work of love, for it so fills the married couple with desire and lust for each other, strengthens and warms the womb, indeed it joins them together in such a way that they hardly need to use it more than once or twice before the woman conceives. However, when you use it, you must add two or three drops of an oil which I will describe after this. I should, of course, have excluded nuns and asked them not to pass on the information to anyone for whom it is unseemly. Nevertheless, I must point out something which has long remained a secret. Therefore I say that if a member of the male sex is too weak and denied the strength to acquire heirs, let him take a little of this pomade, mix three or four drops of proper benzoin oil with it and anoint the place which cannot be named without offending good taste, then he will acquire an unusual lust and desire and will make the womb, which has been cleansed beforehand, as is fitting, capable of conceiving. Similarly, if anyone has spots or ulcers on his face or any other part of his body, if he first adds a little of the other sublimate to this pomade, it will get rid of them, without any harm or ill-effect on the person. Apart from the above-described attributes, the pomade has many others for adorning the complexion and keeping it healthy, spotless, completely flawless and perfect, but you should not, however, use it continuously because it tends to make the face browner rather than whiter, on account of the fat. For to tell the truth, nothing fatty, be it a lotion or what you will, is suitable for beautifying the complexion. It is nevertheless true that it will keep the face looking healthy and spotless, even in winter. If, however, a member of the fairer sex who is old and wrinkled uses it to preserve her complexion, she will appear fully rejuvenated. If, however, she is young, she will appear so from her natural and innate beauty and from her colour. Indeed, if a member of the fairer sex takes a little of this pomade when she comes out of the water or her bathroom,

CLAMVS ODO,
RATVS OFFICI
NARVM

Ool riechen
der calmus

Radix calami odorati
officinarum.

lies in her bed, perspires and applies it to her face, she will change from an ugly Hecuba into an exceedingly beautiful Polyrena. Finally, if this pomade has been prepared correctly, it will not go musty, however old it may be. If it were old, you could mix up two drachms of this pomade and half of a third of a drachm each of musk and grey amber, but it is not advisable to do that, though if you were to do it, it is not inefficacious mixed like that.

❧ HOW TO PREPARE BENZOIN OIL,

which has the most wonderful scent, in such a way that it also acts as a base for all precious perfumes. For above all one must think of what epitomizes the loveliness of perfume, apart from natural balsam and oil of amber. As you will see, that which is awarded the prize is called Ros Syriacus. *It has not been seen for a very long time, however, so nothing can compare with it except oil from grey amber.*

T ake about a pound and a half of real, genuine benzoin, grind it down roughly and put it into a retort. Bury the latter in ashes or finely sifted sand inside an earthenware pot, place the pot on top of an oven, specially made for the purpose, and, if you have taken care with the retort and set it up properly, place the cover on top of it. Take care that it totally encloses the spout of the retort, then seal it with strips of leather, which have been well smeared with egg-white, so that the smell cannot escape, for if that were to happen in the slightest degree, many people would find it very disagreeable and consider it to be an awful smell, particularly someone who is by nature prone to coughing. Once you have sealed the retort in this manner, make a small fire and then feed it vigorously with kindling, without pausing, and soon you will see a yellow liquid flowing out – not much to begin with, but anyhow this is of no great value. After this, snow-like steam or mist will appear and collect around the neck of the retort. Then use the bellows more strongly and as soon as all the snow

MARVM DIOSCORIDIS   klein maioran

has collected up by the neck of the retort, so that you might think it will block the tube, although that is not the case, the intense steam created by the fire will be sufficiently powerful to flow through into the collecting vessel and actually looks like a tallow candle. Then make a more intense fire and a black, strongly perfumed oil will drip out; do not let the fire go out until you see there is no further precipitation. Then let it cool down a little and remove the collecting vessel or receptacle and take out the snow which resembles a candle, for this is the definitive essence of this oil. Those who sell red benzoin oil do not prepare it from a single ingredient, but from several, as follows. If you would like to make it, and it is indeed the most excellent and, at the same time, the main base for all other exquisite perfumes, then take two drachms of the said snow and four ounces of fresh, new, sweet almond oil. Dissolve both in an earthenware dish over hot ashes, frequently stirring with a spatula until the snow is well and truly dissolved, and if you want to turn it red while it is dissolving, add a little of the root of the true alkanet to it. That is how to prepare it. And if you would like to prepare a very precious oil or water for a noble lady or a noble lord, one which has a most excellent scent, then add a drachm of grey amber to four ounces of the said snow and you will obtain an oil the like of which is not to be found in the world, so fine and precious is it. If, however, the black oil has settled on the bottom of the receptacle and has a very strong scent, it may be mixed with liquid storax to make exceptionally good musk apples or balls.

❦ HOW TO MAKE A PRECIOUS NUT-
MEG OIL, *which is not only just as potent
and effective as nutmeg but, in addition, when
applied to the stomach, helps get rid of nausea,
retching and all kinds of pains in that area.*

T ake half a pound of nutmegs, grind them coarsely
and let them boil in a pan with half a quart of well
water. When the mixture has boiled from one to
four times, remove it from the fire and put it into
a small, new muslin bag. Tie it up firmly and put it in a press
which closes well. Put a dish underneath and let what is pressed
out run into it. You will then see the oil floating on the water
like yellow wax, having an exquisitely fine scent. If you keep
it for a year, the yellow will turn a dark-brown colour, but the
longer it is kept, the more delightful the perfume. You will not
get more than an ounce from half a pound of nutmegs. Since
it produces such a small quantity of oil, it can be made another
way. This, though, is the proper and most natural way and it
is thoroughly comparable in potency with artificial balsam.

❦ HOW TO PREPARE THE BEST BASE FOR AROMATIC POWDERS, *possessing a pleasing and long-lasting perfume, which is not at all difficult. It can, however, be prepared only once a year.*

Take one ounce of green cypress-wood shavings, six ounces of Florentine violet roots, three ounces of cloves, three drachms of sweet flag and six drachms of wild olive wood and pulverize them. Take care, however, not to make too much dust. Next, before the dew has fallen on them, take 300 or 400 fresh and perfectly clean black orchids, crush them well with a wooden pestle in a marble mortar and pour a little rose-water over them. When everything has been well and truly pounded, make small, round biscuits out of the mixture and dry them in the shade, then they will give off a very lovely perfume. From this preparation may also be made aromatic soaps, cypress powder, violet root powder, musk heads, aromatic wafers and other sweet-smelling things. In order to make such a mixture even more exquisite, you can add as much musk and grey amber as you are able or desire. Wherever these two substances come together, I have no doubt there will be a most pleasant and acceptable perfume. This will also occur if they are pounded, finely ground and mixed with rose-water and allowed to dry in the shade. Apart from the delightful scent, however, given off by the said composition, if you carry the biscuits around or even put a little of one in your mouth, you will have a pleasant aroma for the whole day. Or if someone's mouth smells, because the teeth are bad, or if someone has a foul-smelling sore on the body or something

MÁRTIA VIOLA PVRPVREA. ongefult wolfmeck end bra
ODORA SIMPLEX merkē veiel.

1

else unpleasant, which causes him to shun the proximity of people, he will have such a pleasant aroma about him that no one will know the cause of it.

At the time of the pestilence there was no perfume in the world better able to drive away the evil and poisonous air. As proof of this I would mention that in AD 1546 I was recruited and employed by the authorities and municipality of Aix-en-Provence to preserve their health. It was so bad in that place and the pestilence had such a powerful hold that it lasted from the end of May to the ninth month, during which time countless people, both young and old, died from eating and drinking. The churchyards were so full of dead bodies that there was no more consecrated ground in which to bury them. Among them were many who were robbed of their senses overnight and those to whom this happened had no external marks. Those, however, who had ulcers of plague spots died suddenly, yet they had talked without any alteration in their speech. However, after death their bodies were soon covered with black spots. Those who died in a state of madness had drinking wells which were beautifully clear like white wine, but after they departed this life half their bodies turned sky blue, suffused with violet-blue blood. These people were so infectious that if anyone went within five yards of them, he would be visibly affected and very soon infected. Many of them had carbuncles on their front and back and all over their feet. Those who had them on their back became swollen, but the majority of them got better, whereas not one of those who had them on their front improved or recovered. At the onset of the sickness a few people had marks behind their ears, although they continued living for six days. I was curious as to why more of them died on the sixth, rather than the seventh day. The reason was that this sickness itself played such a violent and tyrannical role. However, when it started no one was spared and the same was true in the middle of its course. The permitted remedies, purging medicines and the like, were of no use at all. Similarly authentic and correctly made Venetian treacle was of no use, for the virulence and raging of the sickness was so great that no one among them was able to escape it. Similarly, when one went through the whole town visiting the places and dwellings of the afflicted people and threw them out, the following morning there were just as many sick as there had been previously.

There proved to be no better medicine in the world for the said disease than this composition, because all those who carried it with them or had some in their mouth survived. When the disease finally abated, it was shown from experience that the concoction had indeed saved a countless number of lives. Although there is little agreement about the substance of which we are speaking here, it is not inappropriate to recount the usefulness and benefits of it for those who used it during the said poisonous sickness. For the plague which raged at the time was so infectious that it was a terrible thing. Many said it was a punishment sent specially by God, for only a mile away from the town everyone was fit and healthy. The inhabitants of the town, however, were so poisoned by it that, as soon as someone who was not affected with the disease looked at them, he would immediately become infected by it. There were a lot of provisions to hand – everything necessary to sustain human life and costing very little. Death, however, was so remorseless towards them that even parents ceased to care for their children. Yes indeed, many left wife and child when they saw that they had been attacked and infected by this disease, under the influence of which many, in their confusion and irrational behaviour, threw themselves into the wells, while others fell from windows. Some who had marks on their shoulders and on their chests suffered such serious bleeding day and night from their noses that it caused their death. Pregnant women gave birth too soon and died

27

ROSAE DOMESTICAE RVBEAE
ET CANDIDAE . AC SYLVESTRES
PRIMAE:

Zam Rosn rot vnd weyß
auch heckrosen

within four days, while the children died very quickly and one could see that the whole of their bodies was covered with blue spots and it looked as if they were suffused with blood. In short, the misery was so great that frequently someone who had gold and silver also died, since there was no one on hand to give him a drink of fresh water. When, for example, I prescribed medicine for someone, it would certainly be brought to them, but the misery was such that many died while they still had the medicine in their mouth. Although I should like to give a full account of what happened during the course of this pestilence, that would be inappropriate in this present work so, as is my custom, I will describe for you how to prepare a powder from the roots of violets – one which has a very exquisite scent. If you make it according to my instructions, you will find it extraordinarily agreeable, for our composition from roses makes it very pleasant.

❦ HOW TO MAKE AN AROMATIC, LONG-LASTING PASTE, *which is very easy and suitable for forming musk beads and paternoster beads. To all aromatic mixtures are added roses, which are the best things for imparting scent, although they soon lose it on account of their subtle and delicate substance. Thanks to this composition, however, the musk apples and paternoster beads retain their perfume for a very long time. It is not possible, however, to prepare the paste more frequently than once a year.*

Take about 500 or 600 clean, red black orchids, as many as you will, and pour as much water over them as you think necessary for the mixture to boil. Bring it to the boil five or six times, put it in a new earthenware pot and let it stand for twenty-four hours. The following day heat it up again and squeeze it as much as possible in a press until all the goodness has come out and nothing is left except the withered orchids. Then take the liquid, put it into a cauldron and let it boil on a low fire, but start it off slowly and increase the heat towards the end until the vapour has been dispersed. When you eventually see that the vapour is slowly diminishing, stir the liquid with a piece of wood or stick and when you see that it is as thick as boiled honey, drain it into a glazed, earthenware dish and place it in the sun for a few days. This composition will now have a very pleasant perfume and keep for a long while.

❧ ANOTHER DESCRIPTION *of how to make aromatic balls. Although many people have made and prepared aromatic apples or balls, one doing it this way and another that, I advise you to follow the example of the renowned painter Zeusi from Heraklion.*

W hen this man had memorized the appearance of many beautiful young women, he took the nose from one, the mouth from another, the cheeks from a third and from the others whatever seemed good to him. Then, so I believe, when he had got all these attributes well and truly fixed in his mind, he created from them a woman, comparable in beauty to the Greek Helen, indeed even preferable to her, and whoever wanted to look at her had to pay a small piece of silver. Similarly, those who wish to make a good sweet-scented apple or ball must use the best possible ingredients, as far as the scent is concerned, and make a confection or composition which will be agreeable and keep for a long time. For to do otherwise would be to have a body without a soul. You must not, however, include any ingredient the scent of which is too strong or sharp or stands out too much, because it might cause a headache or some indisposition on the part of a woman. The result will be a very pleasant mixture which will retain its perfume for a long time and, purely from the point of view of its scent, is similar to musk.

Take two ounces of the purest labdanum gum, one ounce each of gum storax and the aromatic gum which we call benzoin, half an ounce of rose troches, one ounce of violet

LIMONIA MALVS.

Limonbaum

III

root powder and half a drachm each of musk and amber. Beat everything into a powder, knead it together with the said mixture of roses for a whole hour and you will have a pleasant-smelling, exquisite apple, the like of which cannot be found elsewhere in the world. Those who master this art will sing its praises loud and long. Many people have added white or red sandalwood to it, which has no merit, just like many other things which have no delicate scent but smell more of medicines and apothecaries' premises. Nevertheless, it is right to pardon and forgive someone who errs and strays from the road and commits to writing or print what he neither knows nor has ever learned. For in matters appertaining to external adornment or attire he has written things which have neither beginning nor end nor any justifiable basis. Thus you should know that labdanum is very good when it is not adulterated and is the substance, obtained from goats' beards in the fortunate lands of Arabia, about which Herodotus wrote in his third book. I discovered this three years ago, after extensive research throughout the city of Genoa, and brought back with me half a pound, on account of its beneficial properties. For in Arabia it is collected from the stomachs of goats and sheep, in the same way that sheeps' wool is acquired here in Provence. When the labdanum is of good quality and unadulterated, they make balls out of it because, regardless of the fact that they have a very pleasant scent, nothing is better for protecting one against infection in times of pestilence or during outbreaks of dangerous illnesses. For it cheers up humans, strengthens the heart and the brain and is extremely efficacious against fainting attacks, and if anyone's heart is causing problems, it has such a lovely perfume that the more you hold it to your nose, the more pleasant and attractive it is. It also strengthens the brain in cases of epilepsy and protects a sufferer to such an extent that in cases where someone used to have an attack once a month, he can subsequently go for three months without a single one.

CCCXLII.   292   373.

HAS GERMANICA PRIMA.   spicanardi.

VII.

❦ POWDER FOR CLEANING THE TEETH *and whitening them in a few days, so that, no matter how discoloured they may be, they will appear like ivory and the breath will smell sweet.*

T ake three drachms each of crystal, flint, white marble, glass and calcined rock salt, two drachms each of calcined cuttlefish bone and small sea-snail shells, half a portion each of pearls and fragments of gemstones, two drachms of the small white stones which are to be found in running water, a scruple of amber and twenty-two grains of musk. Mix them well together and grind them into the finest powder on a marble slab. Rub the teeth with it frequently and, if the gums have receded, paint a little rose honey on them. The flesh will then grow back in a few days and the teeth will be perfectly white.

❦ ANOTHER EXCELLENT METHOD *of cleaning the teeth, even when they are rotten and almost completely decayed, for if they have been tarnished for a long while, it is impossible to whiten them, but with this method you will soon see a result.*

Take some of the expanding clay, of the type used for bricks which are white when fired. Take as much as you like. Knead it well for a good while, until it is entirely free from lumps, and when you have done that, make it into small, long, round pieces. Dry these in the sun and, when they are well dried, bake them in an oven used for clay pots or tiles. To speed up the process, either place them on an iron plate, a tile or a building stone and take them to a blacksmith's smithy. There go to work with the bellows and blow for a quarter of an hour, and when they are completely fired, as if they had spent three days in the oven, when that stage is reached, then prepare some water. Soak them and, because the newly fired clay draws the water into itself, it will retain the aroma internally. Nevertheless, if you use it for cleaning your teeth, it will get rid of the unclean rottenness and the evil smell and give the mouth a pleasant aroma for the whole day. If you do this frequently, your teeth will become as white as ivory, no matter how discoloured they may have been beforehand. It would also not be bad if, after they have been frequently cleaned with the sweet-smelling water, they should first be treated with egg-white, in which a gold leaf has been placed, in order that they may acquire a better lustre.

❦ A METHOD OF PREPARING WATER
TO SOFTEN AND MOISTEN THE BODY

Take four ounces of Florentine violet roots, one ounce of red black orchids and a similar quantity of cloves, six drachms of wild lilies, a measure of cinnamon, half an ounce of sweet flag, a measure of lavender flowers, three drachms of marjoram, two drachms of bitter orange peel, one ounce of storax, a measure of grey amber and half a drachm of musk. Grind them all to powder and put it into a Venetian glass container, together with some good rose-water and bitter-orange blossom-water or some made from lime or lemon blossom, for they are equally efficacious. Use more of the bitter-orange blossom-water, but of the two latter do not have more than a pound of sixteen ounces. Then leave the mixture to stand for four days before taking a glass container, which is more than half the size of the original, and pouring the mixture into it. Take care to shake the original container well and when you have poured in as much as you want, allow your potion to draw in it for more or less an hour, as you see fit. Make sure, however, that you keep the glass properly covered and closed, so that nothing can waft out. Now when it has thoroughly absorbed the water, then paint it either on all your teeth or perhaps half of them, whichever you think best, and clean them with it. So that the contamination will be washed away when you have used the potion, take the water remaining in the bottom of the container, strain it through a cloth, as one does with the hippocras, and squeeze it out well and truly at the bottom, and keep doing this until you see that it is clear and clean. You can use this water in many ways to provide a pleasant perfume, whether it be for the face, the hands or the beard or for washing around the mouth.

ALTHAEA DIOSCO-
RIDIS

Gemainer eybiſch.

❦ HOW TO MAKE AN AROMATIC OIL,

the wonderful and powerful scent of which is not to be found in the whole world or obtained from any doctor.

This oil is also numbered among those which in olden days were used by heathen kings for their best perfumes. Apart from that, however, this scent has very great virtues. So, for example, it will warm the womb of an unfruitful woman in such a manner and prepare it so that if one spreads only about a single drop on it, there is no doubt that she will become pregnant, no matter how weak the man may be. He, too, can use it in a similar manner, no matter if he is old, past his prime and of little use, for it will warm him as well, without adversely affecting his prowess. Anyone wishing to use it on his or her own person for the sake of its perfume alone should, if a woman, put a little on her temples, or if a man, rub it on his beard, and it will give off such a powerful and strong scent that it will be smelt as soon as the person steps into the street. It will last for more than ten days. It is true that it is expensive, but its perfume is so lovely that it cannot be bought for any amount to money, not to mention the fact that it drives away the foulest of harmful air.

This, then, is the composition.

Take about twelve ounces of occidental grey amber (do not be put off by the fact that you need so much, for the child which it will bear will delight you so much it will more than repay you), round about four ounces of best oriental musk, which is red in colour, half a pound of finely crushed cloves, four ounces of the inner bark of the best cinnamon, two ounces of Florentine violet roots, one ounce of spikenard and half a pound of the most delicate wild olive wood. Mix all these ingredients carefully and pulverize them. Put the mixture into a small retort, whether you wish to make a lot or a little, and place it inside a pot or earthenware vessel in which you have previously placed sifted ashes. Bury the retort up to its neck and heat an oven made for the purpose. When the oven is properly dry, put the cooking vessel inside it and seal it with well-mixed lime. Now get the fire going underneath it so that it starts off gently but is going more vigorously towards the end. Keep it going until all the precipitation has stopped and you will be able to differentiate between three or four different substances. First to be exuded will be a black oil of such a lively, exquisite and sharp perfume that it is impossible to find any water, or natural or artificial balsam to compare with it. When you have almost come to the end, make up a good strong fire, but not too fierce, not because it would damage the perfume or detract from it, but because the residue left at the bottom when nothing more is coming out is just as highly prized as the oil. For out of it you can make aromatic powders, balls, paternoster beads or other compositions, fit for kings and other great princes and lords. When you are half way through the process, however, change the cooking vessel if you think it would be a good idea, but if you do not, draw the oil off once. If, on the other hand, you do not want to distil it through a retort, do so through a small glass phial which is only half full when all the ingredients have been put into it, so that it does not overflow while being boiled. Distil it until nothing remains except the pot, which will have as powerful a scent as the oil and be even more pungent, so that you can fumigate gloves in it or make a regal odour, with which none may easily compare.

TICVM DVARVM ET SEPTVA
NTA SPICARVM.

weitze mit zway vnd siben
zig ehern.

IIII

❧ DEAR FRIENDLY READER, *at this point, not without very good reasons, I have omitted from my translation into German the eighteenth chapter, because it teaches such things as are not fitting for a Christian or God-fearing man to know and I therefore felt it better not to make any mention of them.*

❦ HOW TO MAKE AN AROMATIC SOAP
which makes the hands white and soft and which has a sweet and pleasant perfume.

Take some yew root, scrape it without washing it and dry it in the shade. Next pulverize it and take four ounces of it, one ounce of starch flour, one ounce of wheat flour, six drachms of ground pine-nut kernels, two ounces of almond kernels from which the oil has been well pressed, one ounce and a half of clean bitter-orange pips, two ounces each of oil of tartar and sweet almond oil and a half drachm of musk. Grind these up into the finest possible powder and for every ounce of this powder add half an ounce of Florentine violet roots. Next, take a further half-pound of yew root and let it soak overnight in good-quality rose-water or bitter-orange blossom-water. Squeeze the water and roots thoroughly and knead the exuded slime with the other ingredients. Add the musk and make the mixture into globes or round balls. Dry them and when you want to use them, take one in your hand, pour water over it and rub your hands with it and they will become white and tender and soft. Gaetan soap, however, is excluded, though others do use it, for although it whitens the hands, it also makes them rough and dry or chapped, because it is made from a strong, sharp lye, namely from the chalk of ordinary silica ashes, from which glass is made, and the ashes of burnt tartar. Gaetan soap has, however, been made from chalk and burnt tartar for a very long while and, although that soap is prepared from this lye and from ordinary olive oil, it still makes the hands very rough. Our composition for soap, however, is very gentle and pleasant, for only mild substances are used in it and even if the hands are already hard, after using it two or three times they will become as gentle and soft as if they were the hands of a young girl of ten.

STICHAS GERMANICA ALTERA LAVADVLAVE   Lauendel.

V.

❦ ANOTHER AROMATIC SOAP *for the beard, which is used by the nobility and is very pleasant.*

Take half a pound of Gaetan soap, or one of the whitest you can obtain, and cut the whole lot into flakes with a knife. Next take two and a half ounces of finely pulverized Florentine violet roots, six drachms each of sweet flag and marjoram, half an ounce of dried roses and a similar amount of cloves, a drachm of fresh coriander, one and a half drachms each of lavender flowers and bay leaves and three drachms of gum storax. Grind everything to powder and knead it together with the soap flakes. Then take ten grains each of musk and amber, temper it with rose-water and shape soap balls out of it, which are excellent for washing the beard. If, however, you wish to wash your face with it, when you are kneading it add a small quantity, or about an ounce, of sweet almond oil. That will make it somewhat milder and make the face tender and soft and not drawn. One comes across many people who are so inquisitive and want to know how to make ordinary soap, which is in fact something which is more the business of artisans, but I have not included it here, in spite of the fact that in many places they are not able to make it because the oil is difficult to obtain – for the most important ingredient in it is the oil and oil jars. From the soap it is also possible to make a material of which goldsmiths can make good use instead of borax, if that is not available. That is why we will set down its description, for this borax is one of the most excellent ingredients for adorning the face and whitening it, which is why I thought it useful to put it down in writing here. When all the deceitful and lying alchemists have described how to make borax, they have never known what was the principal or main ingredient in it. And so that I may be of use to many people who would like to know what this might be, it is none other than the lye, or what the false alchemists call the capitellum, which is the most important and principal ingredient in the soap and if you want to make a proper borax, do it as follows.

LAVRVS TENVIFOLIA.　　schmalbletterter Lorbeerbaum.

I.

❦ HOW TO MAKE ARTIFICIAL BORAX,
which may be purer than candied sugar.

Take two or three pounds, or as much as you like, of hard Gaetan or similar soap and chop it up into small pieces. Put these into a new earthenware pot and let them boil with half a pound of butterfat. When you notice that it is almost beginning to burn, put another half pound in and let it burn, so that it all turns black. Take the burnt residue and pulverize it, for the best results grinding it down in goats' or cows' milk. When you have done this, let it come to the boil four times in the said goats' milk before letting it stand for a while. Remove the scum, which is merely milk, and put the mixture into a new earthenware pot. Put small reeds or the twigs of fir trees into it, so that it adheres to them like candied sugar, and leave it outside or in a cool place for a night or two. If there is a new moon that night or the north wind is blowing, it will freeze like ice, although it will not be as white. As for its effect, it will outlast all metals, including gold and silver. You should not, however, be surprised that such an insignificant ingredient such as soap is the main base and substance of borax and that it caused me a great deal of expense before I discovered that fact. Meanwhile, I was warned that it would not go well with me were I to take my quill in my hand to reveal that. Therefore I will not dwell on it further on this occasion, but revert to our previous topic – how to beautify the face.

❦ HOW TO INTRODUCE GOLD HIGHLIGHTS IN THE HAIR, *no matter whether it is white or black, so that the colour is not soon lost and is retained in its entirety and indeed grows so that it appears yellow at the roots as well as at the ends.*

Take a pound of finely pulverized beech-wood shavings, half a pound of box-wood shavings, four ounces of fresh liquorice, a similar amount of very yellow, dried lime peel, four ounces each of swallow wort and yellow poppy seeds, two ounces of the leaves and flowers of glaucus, a herb which grows in Syria and is akin to a poppy, half an ounce of saffron and half a pound of paste made from finely ground wheat flour. Put everything into a lye made with sieved wood ashes, bring it partly to the boil and then strain the whole mixture. Now take a large earthenware pot and bore ten or twelve holes in the bottom. Next take equal parts of vine ash and sieved wood ash, shake them into a large wooden vessel or mortar, whichever you think better, moisten them with the said lye, thoroughly pulverize the mixture, taking almost a whole day to do this – but make sure that it becomes a bit stiff. Next pound rye and wheat straw in with it until the straw has absorbed the greater part of the lye. Shake these pounded ashes into the said earthenware pot and push an ear of rye into each small hole. Put the straw and ashes in the bottom, so that the pot is filled, though still leaving sufficient space for the remainder of the lye to be poured over the mixture. Towards evening set up another earthenware pot and let the lye run into it through the holes with the ears of rye. When you want to use the lotion, take the liquid which ran out, smear your hair with it and let it dry. Within three or four days the hair will look as yellow as if it were golden ducats. However, before you use it, wash your head with a good lye, because if it were greasy and dirty it would not take the colour so well. You should note that this preparation will last for a year or two and, if one goes about it properly, it can help ten or twelve members of the fairer sex, for very few things will colour the hair. However, one should not allow another man to use it, for anyone with coal-black hair would soon have it gold-coloured and it would remain so for a very long time.

ABIES FOEMINA RVBRA.   Rote dann weiblin.

III.

❦ ANOTHER WAY *of making the hair of the beard blond or golden and of safely getting rid of all kinds of excesses from the body, which disfigure the face. It must, however, be used with discretion, otherwise it may do harm.*

Take two pounds of saltpetre and a pound each of alum and vitriol, mix them and distil the mixture in a glass retort in the following manner. Place the retort containing the said ingredients in a large earthenware vessel or pot and well and truly cover it with ashes, so that it does not break because of the fire. Then cover the cooking vessel and seal it thoroughly with egg-white, quicklime or clay, so that there is no way that air can reach the contents. When the seal has then dried, begin with a small fire and build it up until everything is distilled. You will then have a water which may be compared with aqua regia, but to tell the truth there is a slight difference, for this water will break down all kinds of metals and separates gold and silver, which we do not need in this instance; we merely wish to demonstrate that it dyes hair and does not dry it out, as some might maintain, but also produces gold highlights, if it is used in the following manner.

How one should use this water.

When you have washed your head and it is no longer oily or greasy but has been exceptionally well dried, take this water and streak it on your hair and rub it in well without pausing. Take care that it does not touch the scalp, otherwise it would certainly burn it and also damage the hair as if it had been scorched. But if you quickly rub the water in well, so that it has no cause to adhere to it for long and to bespatter or disfigure your complexion, rather than beautify it, then it will make your hair as yellow as threads of gold and will not have a single detrimental effect. Similarly, if a spot or red mole is present, naturally or unnaturally, anywhere you like on your body, or perhaps it has been inherited, if you were to spread only a little of the said water upon it and rub it in rapidly and vigorously and do not give it a chance to take root, then it would get rid of it painlessly without any after-effects. This must, however, be done when the blemishes are still small, otherwise it could hurt to get rid of them. Anyone using this water for spots on the face should not leave his or her apartment for several days, for before the red moles disappear, the water makes them turn yellow like saffron, which neither soap nor water will get rid of until, after several days, a small scab comes off the place touched by the water, underneath which is new, tender and delicate skin. Anyone using this water other than in the manner described will not find that it does them any good. The aqua regia used by goldsmiths is good, but it does not produce anything like the beautiful yellow colour, because it does not use vitriol, for where foreign metal is present with the gold, it breaks it down and it loses weight. So, if you would now like your hair to have the colour you desire, follow the instructions I have given you and do so with sense and understanding, otherwise it will not work and your efforts will have been in vain. The surest way, though, would be for you to use our first water, which I described to you earlier, as it is the safest and has no disadvantages. It is true that the second water makes the hair beautiful and yellow in one day, but it conceals something else within itself and it is essential, therefore, that I describe its potency and effect, so that I can avoid and circumvent any complaint. For if you use this water just as it is, you will find that its potency and effect are entirely different from those described. It takes a great deal of skill to make it suitable for

304

CCXCII
407.

CVS SATIVA

Feigenbaum

noble lords and princes, just as this present small book has been written only at the behest of a mighty princess, for whose pleasure I have most humbly collected many excellent and exceptional arts dealing with how members of the fairer sex may beautify and whiten their complexion – for if a lady is white, she is soon beautiful as well.

A COMPOSITION FOR MAINTAINING THE HEALTH OF THE HUMAN BODY, *which is very potent and effective.*

I will here set down details of a composition which I have often prepared for my gracious Lord Bishop of Carcassonne, Ammanien de Poys, and which has sustained his life. Since the soul of medicine is none other than natural heat and when that ceases, life lingers no longer, so, by means of this composition, a melancholy complexion is changed into a sanguine one, although the humours of the two are radically opposed to each other. For just as smoke undergoes a transformation from when it is a hot and damp substance to when it becomes soot and cold and dry, with the attributes of earthly things, so this composition rejuvenates the humans who use it. No matter how sad or downhearted a person may be, he will become happy and of good cheer or, if fearful and easily afraid, he will be resolute and courageous or, if he is quiet, he will become loquacious. His natural characteristics will also be changed, for if he is somewhat roguish, he will become kind and gentle, as if he were just thirty years old; if his beard is starting to turn grey, it slows up the ageing process considerably, preserves the complexion but not the years, gladdens the heart and the whole person so completely, as if it were the first day that he had come into the world. It makes the breath smell very sweet, to the considerable satisfaction of the person concerned, and does not cause any unnatural fever or make one feel unwell. It checks headaches, drives away pains in the side and greatly increases the production of semen. It maintains the four humours in such harmony and uniformity that if we did not possess them from our birth, we might live for ever. But the One who taught us how we are born into the world, He has also taught us to die. The pleasure, however, which this composition brings to a man refreshes him to such an extent that it so lengthens his life and adds so greatly to it that no chance event, however intense it may be, can stop someone who uses it from living as long as the old heathens. For if someone is susceptible to consumption, whatever form it may take, he will escape from its danger and be free of it. It also protects people from the noisome pestilence and if someone has been infected, though for not longer than ten hours, he will survive. For greater safety, though, he should go at least three miles from the unclean and polluted place, then he will be certain that it will pose no danger or cause after-effects. Thus its properties deserve great praise. Take care, however, to make it as I shall now describe, for there is nothing in it which is impossible to prepare.

This is the composition.

Take the ground spice or the crushed powder of sweet musk, of coral and of dissolved pearls, 150 chopped gold leaves, blue lapis lazuli (which has been washed nine times and prepared and likewise ground into fine powder) – do not, however, use that which the apothecaries have, for that is of no use, but of the kind possessed by those who travel with stones or the ones used by goldsmiths. If you can obtain them, take as much as four drachms, then a drachm each of offcuts or the residue from the five major gems and excellent pearls, three drachms of fine ivory scrapings, one drachm of fine unicorn scrapings, two lots of bone or gristle – more than can be found in a stag's heart – half an ounce each of wild-olive or old wood and the best-quality cinnamon, one ounce each of rose-, alkanet- and violet sugar, six preserved nuts, four ounces of well-preserved candied lemon peel, six drachms of preserved ginger, four ounces of the preserved

EEE 55
EEE

OLVBRINA, SEV SERPENTA
IA SEPLASIARVM FOEMI
NA

natterwurtz weiblin

II

fruit of a foreign tree called myrobalans, of the type known as emblic, one ounce each of finely chopped, preserved bitter oranges, lettuce and pumpkin and four ducats' weight of the best and purest ducat gold you can obtain, together with half an ounce of occidental amber and two drachms of unadulterated musk. Mix the powders or spices together but pound the other ingredients and the gold leaf vigorously in a marble mortar. Then take six ounces of a delicate white silk which has never been used and boil everything in two ounces of kermes' dye, together with half a pound each of the juice of good-smelling apples, roses and blessed thistles and six ounces of the best sugar. Boil them all together until you see that they have turned red, but take care that the sugar is not present when you are boiling the silk. After the silk, the juices, the water and wine have been well boiled, remove them from the fire, filter them carefully and squeeze the liquid out as strongly as you can. Only at this point should you add the sugar to the filtered liquid and boil it like a syrup. When it has boiled well, pour two ounces of the best malmsey over it, or some other good white wine and then let everything boil a little until it turns into a syrup, then take it off the fire and add grey amber to it. If the mixture is correct it will dissolve. When it has cooled, add some musk as well and finally the sugar or conserves and other preserved ingredients and very finely ground spices or powders. Stir the mixture well for half an hour, to enable it to mix all the better, and then take four ounces of preserved alkanet root and one ounce of the finely ground small, sweet spice leopard's-bane. Mix everything thoroughly and finally add the gold leaves. When everything is completed and ready, put it in a tightly closed gold, silver or glass dish.

❦ HOW TO USE THE SAID *composition,*
the potency and effectiveness of which resembles
auro potabilis *or an auric drink.*

Anyone who, each morning an hour and a half before a meal or snack, takes a drachm of this composition with good white wine or malmsey will be protected against all kinds of sickness. For indeed it strengthens the heart and the brain, will get rid of epilepsy in the case of those who are not yet twenty-five years old, rejuvenates people and slows down the ageing process, and if anyone takes it during an epidemic, he will not be infected that day. A crown's weight of this composition provides much more and better potency than a whole capon and so it protects one against leprosy, drives away melancholy and eases stomachache. The greatest virtue which it has, however, is this: if, mixed with alkanet water, it is taken by someone in his last hour, when he is on the point of death and nature and his sickness are doing battle with each other, it will so invigorate and strengthen the patient that the outcome and final judgement on the sickness will be in the patient's favour and nature will obtain the victory. For it strengthens and invigorates the heart 100 times more than Alchermes's confection. In addition, if a woman would like to have children or heirs, it so arranges the male member and the womb that both seeds unite and remain in the bearing place until it is time for the birth. Therefore doctors of medicine, when they think carefully about the effects of this composition, will sing its praises no less than I do. Again, if someone faints and takes only a little of it, he will soon recover his senses. However, this composition is not suitable for everyone, even though we are all human. So if anyone has the desire to live a

233   CXLV.
133.

Semina fabe magne

FABA   BOII

335

long life in happiness and good health, let him have some made up, but at the same time let him be on his guard and not trust every apothecary, for although it is true that there are good ones among them, for every good one there are 100 or 1,000 bad ones. For several among them are not worth what they charge and others, although they have enough money and are of exceedingly good standing, are avaricious, selfish and cunning. For because they are concerned they might not make as much as they would wish, they do not use half or even a third of the ingredients. Many of them are ignorant, incapable and have no desire to learn anything, which is a dreadful crime for such people. Others, however, are very dour and sloveny and act in a very negligent manner with everything they touch. On the other hand, I will not say that there are not some among them who have none of these faults, who in the first place have ability and a good conscience and who are not lacking in skill, but they are careless in their profession and commission anyone with the task, who may carry it out badly. For I must acknowledge that there are some who will do something properly, but they are rare birds and it does not happen very often. Thus I have travelled extensively throughout the whole kingdom of France and have met many apothecaries and become acquainted with them, but I have seen them do so many unspeakable things that I believe one could not find any other trade in which there is more malpractice and conscience so sorely tried. Even if I were to describe just the hundredth part of what I have seen with my own eyes, my paper would melt away. It is not that I particularly wish to cast blame upon certain individuals, for I do not intend to say where such things have happened in order that the sun may seem to shine more brightly upon me, but because I have seen that the world recognizes the characteristics, complexions and skills of all kinds of people and that there are good and bad storms and many places to be explored and herbs to be investigated, which may be useful in one place, but not in another. When I myself was practising medicine, which at the time was my main profession, I came across so much malpractice in so many towns that I gave it up, so that I should not malign anyone. So I will speak of other things, as Lucianus did when he praised Demosthenes, who painted a horse lying on the ground when he wanted, though, to paint it in action. Nevertheless, I have been in many places where the noble art of medicine was very much in fashion and excellent work was carried out, but it does not happen everywhere, as is indeed the case today. Now and then it happens that a doctor goes to an apothecary's premises and, in order to look after his patient's interests, would like to see the medicine himself and weigh out what is necessary, particularly if the apothecary is inexperienced. What happens? If the apothecary happens to be a foolish, proud, seemingly friendly, arrogant, useless, eccentric ass (for good and bad are to be found everywhere), he will reply to this young doctor as follows: 'Why do you want to cause me all this confusion? Do you perhaps think that I am not an honourable man? You should know that I will make it much better than you can prescribe, therefore stick to your own profession and calling and do not interfere with our medicines'! 'Since I will make it better'! − from that and 1,000 other stupid remarks which they make you will understand that I cannot write the twelfth part of the things done by such idiots. It is true, however, that among them I have met very honest and upright men, well versed in their art and exceptionally well instructed in it, who have remained true to it. Among all the places I have visited, however, I know of none where medicine is held in worse esteem and carried out in a more dreadful manner than Marseilles, apart from two or three apothecaries, and the position would be much worse if the doctors of medicine were not so honest and learned.

There is a M. Louis Serre, a renowned and learned man and, like Hippocrates, able to predict the outcome of an illness, who is doing as much as he can there and spares no effort to ensure that everything is done correctly and without deception. If, however, I were to recount here all the places I have repeatedly visited and how medicine is regarded and carried on in each, this book would become much too large. I will, however, single out for praise one man (regardless of the fact that other honourable and just men will not be mentioned in it). He is Joseph Turel Mercur, born at Aix-en-Provence, who is famous both here and elsewhere and currently working with us here at the salon of Francisco Berardus. I am quite prepared to accept that someone might, with justification, say that there are many other places to which I have not been or may have left out, which is what Your Excellency might also have done. That is of course true, for to visit them all would be impossible and human life is short. For I well know that many will not be satisfied, because the evildoers will only gain support and encouragement from it. I have, however, done so for no other reason than to emphasize that if someone wishes the above-mentioned composition to aid or assist him, he must go about things diligently and take care that not the slightest ingredient is omitted, in order to be certain of its efficacy, for it has such a potency that if someone has a very weak heart, it will swiftly penetrate it and prolong the person's life.

389

FAGVS.

BUCHBAUM

❦ HOW TO BLACKEN WHITE HAIR or
the beard.

If you want to blacken white hair on your head or on your beard, and would like to be certain that the colour is fixed and will remain for a long while, then act according to the following instructions. This is the art used by Medea, who was accused of making old people young and creating them anew. The very old Emperor Gordianus used it. He was a son of Metius Marullus, who lived 234 years after the birth of our Saviour Jesus Christ. Thanks to this colour, prepared for him by one of his chamberlains, he still appeared youthful at the age of sixty-three. This, then, is a description of it.

Take two ounces of rock alum, one pound of the extruded sap of the meadow herb which the people of Lorraine use for their pastures, half a pound of the juice of green walnuts, six drachms each of cypress cones, indiarubber-plant leaves and oak apples from a withered oak tree. First put the alum and the meadow-herb sap into vinegar until it is half-saturated, then take this water and when it is heated, wash your beard or the hair on your head with it. Take care, however, not to let it touch the scalp if possible, for it will turn it black. Once you have washed with the first water, boil the oak apples, cypress cones and the indiarubber-plant leaves in the remaining water. Wash the beard with it once more and it will then turn a lovely blackish-brown. Next take the walnut juice and wash your beard thoroughly, taking care not to touch the skin too much, until you see that the hair is turning colour. In order to ensure that the colour of the hair on the head or the beard remains all the longer, take a sponge and dip it in the walnut juice, with which a little alum has been mixed. This is how the colour really gets into the hair. Before doing so, however, the hair must be carefully washed and cleaned with the following soap, for it removes the fat and blackens the hair.

LYCYRRHIZA SATIVA DIOSCORIDIS,
SEV PEREGRINA.

zam frembd füßholtz.

❧ HOW TO MAKE A SOAP *which soon blackens the beard.*

Take half a pound of finely flaked Gaetan soap and let it dissolve in an earthenware vessel over a low fire, always taking care that the fire is not too fierce. As soon as it is dissolved and is beginning to turn black, poke the fire gently and take care that the flames do not flare up. Then take two drachms each of resin soot and black pitch and, as soon as the flames have taken hold, quickly remove the soap and pour it out on to a marble slab and, as you do so, add the said soot. When the mixture has cooled, pound it to powder, knead it with fresh walnut juice, mix a little of the soot with it and make it into small balls, as you see fit. When you want to use these, take some cypress cones, boil them in water with a little vinegar and wash your beard or your hair with the liquid. Then, without pausing, do the same using the soap balls and your beard will become like black amber. Take care, however, that it touches the face as little as possible, not that it would do great harm, but because it would be very difficult to get it clean again. The famous sculptor Myron used this lotion and artifice when he wished to make the beautiful Taidem of Corinth accede to his desires. She, however, did not want to use it on hair, but on the wrinkled face, as the poet Ausonius recounted in his writings. We have now used this daily and are still doing so and one could well say that it was Tiresias who has changed age and generation. If, however, you are not confident about doing everything which has been described, then, so that you do not spoil the whole effect, take some borax instead of soap, for that does not burn too hard. Take care, though, when it begins to turn black, even if no flames get at it, for it is also not good for it to have too little heat, because then the oily moisture could dissolve and if that were to happen there would be no soap. However, once it has been used two or three times – or even on the first occasion – it will change the colour of the beard and it will stay like that for a long time. Take note, however, that once the said soap has blackened the hair, it makes it somewhat rough and coarse, but if you use the following oil, it will make it soft and much blacker than it was before.

❦ A METHOD FOR GETTING RID OF
SPOTS ON THE FACE, *to be used at night
so that they disappear completely and do not
reappear, except when one continually stays out
in the sun. It also rids the face of red moles and
blemishes.*

Take six drachms each of squirting cucumber roots, lily bulbs, daffodil bulbs, the roots of adder's-tongue or cuckoo pint, mallow or ivy with fresh berries, our borax, date stones, bitter-almond kernels and cherry stones, one drachm each of white coral, bean flour, fig-seed flour, crystal, cuttlefish bone, *axungiae vitri*, rock salt, woodbine, gypsum, whitest marble, gluten and juniper berries and half an ounce of white lead. Grind it to a fine powder and, as far as is possible with the metals, soften it and knead it with very fresh oxgall for almost a whole day. Then make small pills from the mixture, each weighing about one drachm. When you want to use one, place it on a piece of marble, mix it with fine honey until it is like a salve and when you go to bed at night, rub your face with it while it is hot. When you get up in the morning, boil some beans, but make sure that no traces of pod remain and that they have previously been soaked in water until they are half-saturated. While the water is still hot, wash your face with it, then dry it with a sponge which has been moistened with white wine, rose-water and spittle. If you do not want it to have such a sheen, use only the rose-water. When you look in a mirror you will wonder where the spots on your face have gone. It is suspected that this is what Dioscorides used when the heat of the sun brought him out in spots while he was looking for

ALOE CVM
FLORIBVS.

Aloen mit blumen

II

herbs. I have used it in Savona for the wife, now a widow, of M. Bernard Grass and for the bride of M. Johan Ferlin of Carmignol. You should have seen the wonderful things it achieved in the course of one night. I had intended to use it on several people in the neighbourhood, but I have to say that I live among simple people who have nothing in common with educated people and are extraordinarily inexperienced in all the liberal arts.

❦ A LOTION FOR WHITENING THE FACE *and keeping it beautiful for a long time, in order also to give it a natural pallor and whiteness, which needs repeated application. For this reason one must use it for four days. It is also for simple people and those of the lower class. However, I have also used it on people of higher degree who have been very pleased with it and think no less of it than of the very carefully prepared sublimate.*

Take two ounces each of white, well-cleaned wild lentils, lily bulbs, both adders'-tongues, starch, Venetian white lead (frequently washed with rose-water), Gaetan soap, rice and shelled sweet-almond kernels. Steep them all together and then put the mixture into a pristine earthenware pot with an earthenware lid. Place it in an oven used for making bread and leave it there until it is baked. Then take it out and put it into a glass container again. Next, take one ounce each of arabian gum and tragacanth and half a small quart each of marigold- and white-lily-water and leave the gum to steep in it overnight. Then take six drachms of fine white sea shells or porcelain and pound them to powder, grinding them down completely in lime juice. Next take half an ounce of borax and mix everything together apart from the gum, but it would be good if you were able to grind that down finely as well. Add some of our pomade and stir it up well in a marble mortar. Then pour over it a little of the slime of white poplar roots, which have been steeped in rose-water and black-coriander-seed-water. Mix everything thoroughly and make a salve with it. At night when you go to bed, apply it to your face hot or lukewarm and leave it until morning. Then boil some beans in water and wash your face until you have removed the salve. Then go over your face once more with a sponge moistened with rose-water and let it dry, but take care nothing is left behind which might have an adverse effect. The gum, which strongly adheres to the face, nevertheless imparts to it a natural lustre, which is visible for all to see. For that reason both these gums should be beautiful and white, especially the tragacanth. If the work is carried out as instructed, overnight the complexion will be so changed that in the morning an old woman will look like a young girl.

167

479.

COLOCYNTHIS OB/
LONGA GLABRA VARI/
EGATA.

Lange glatte gesprengte
coloquint.

VIII.

BOOK TWO

❦ MICHEL NOSTRADAMUS

Doctor of Medicine, wishes the best of good fortune and health to Jean Nostradamus, Procurator in the parliament at Aix-en-Provence.

So that I may satisfy the wishes and desires of many honourable people, including members of the fairer sex, who always desire to learn and experience new things and like to have their store chests full of all kinds of preserved fruits, and also those countless other women who live in great splendour in the country and possess a considerable surplus of all kinds of fruits, and with the aim of showing how to refresh and sustain the human body, but one thing is necessary and yet relatively straightforward. That is how to conserve various fruits so that they will keep for a long while without changing except for their appearance and lose any bad or unpleasant taste and, by means of a liquid, acquire a sweetness which drives away any natural bitterness, and, through the use of honey and sugar, take on the desired qualities. For if someone wishes to keep the fruits grown in the garden just as they are, they will soon go rotten, because some are very succulent and some have very little sap and need moisture. If, however, they are preserved in sugar, that will protect them against decay and they will acquire a very desirable sweet taste. In cases of necessity the human body receives more strength from a small quantity of such fruits than from many other foods. So, particularly in the country, there are many people who have very large and vast stores of fruits, just like bees which are always making honey. Those who lack honey have a surplus of must, which they are able to use in place of sugar or honey without any ill-effect or disadvantage. For what is preserved in boiled must is just as nourishing as that preserved in the best sugar. It may not be as delicate and fine, but one often thinks more of a thing which one has made oneself at home for little expenditure than if it

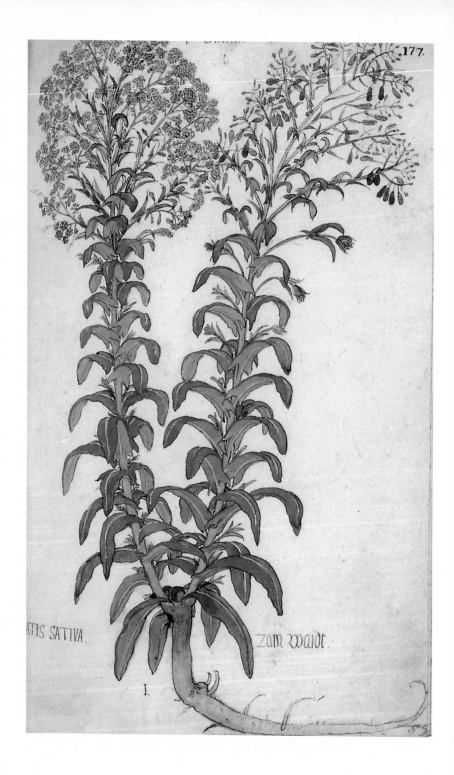

ATIS SATIVA.

zam waidt.

I.

had come from the Orient or Valencia in Spain, the former being better than the latter. As far as that is concerned, though, neither the famous city of Genoa nor the incomparable city of Venice has an advantage. In other matters, though, it would be tiresome to listen to comparisons. In all honesty, however, I have often seen preserved things from Valencia which were extraordinarily good. Their sugar is cheaper than ours, but they are more skilled in the art of preservation.

The same is true of their sweetmeats, in the manner in which they finish them, for when the sugar has been thoroughly absorbed and all bad and harmful moisture has been removed, they completely get rid of this sugar (which has become blackened through repeated boiling) and use a very beautiful one, which then makes the confectionery exceptionally attractive and excellent. I have written something about this for the benefit of those who never leave their towns and like to give the impression that they know a great deal, though frequently shamefully deceiving themselves. If, in their spare time, they have a desire to find out about such things, they will not regret having paid to acquire the book. Also many people who would like to preserve something in sugar do not have an apothecary or spice merchant to hand, and it often happens that one falls into the hands of a master or an apprentice who thinks he knows a lot but frequently knows nothing at all, and the sugar and honey burn and the confectionery is spoilt, so that it has to be thrown away. In order to counteract and obviate these deficiencies, whether they are serious, merely slight or occur frequently, read this book and search out in it the place where you will find the description of the confection you desire to make and you will be able to prepare it properly and well. If you make it according to the instructions, you will find that in goodness and attractiveness there will be no difference between it and the versions from Spain and Italy which are available in France. If, however, you should wish to cut down on the amount of sugar you use, the taste will still make it worthy of the name, but if you want to delight the eye and the mouth you must do as instructed, just like someone wanting to make a proper salad who is not parsimonious with the oil, so you ought not to try to save on sugar. And when you have made something beautiful, its attractiveness, goodness and taste will be all the greater. For those, however, who do not wish to do it as suggested or do not have the ability to use sugar or honey in this manner, for them I have included details of how to make a boiled wine which was used by the most distinguished and noble Romans and called by them defrutum, which was none other than a boiled must, as thick as honey, without the addition of other ingredients. For although they had considerable knowledge and were unspeakably rich, they were nevertheless very happy to use this liquid, because it came from the fields which they themselves cultivated, as Marcus Varro described at great length when he wrote to his lady wife, Fundaria. One will therefore find a lot of people who make this boiled must during the grape harvest and get by with it throughout the year, instead of sugar or honey, and even prefer to use it for preserving purposes. For this reason I am sure that you gentlemen who have already studied this branch of medicine will not blame me for seeking to instruct in these matters, in our own language, the many people who understand nothing about medicine and who do not know how to preserve their fruits skilfully. For even if there are some people who are displeased by this, there will be a whole host of those who are pleased.

253

CVPRESSVS ARBOr FOEMINA.

Cypreßbaum weiblin.

❧ THE SECOND PART OF THIS *small book, in which are included the way, method and manner of preserving all kinds of fruits in sugar, honey and boiled wine. Together with two ways of making purging rose juice, and also candied sugar, penide sugar and Spanish turron.*

❦ HOW TO PRESERVE LEMON PEEL *or*
the inner part of the fruit.

Take a whole lemon and, according to size, cut it lengthwise into six or seven parts or pieces, so that each segment is at least two fingers' width. When you have chopped it up, fill an earthenware (or any other kind of) pot with water. Peel the skin from the pieces, making sure that there is no flesh attached; take care, too, that the peel is not too thick and is as long as the lemon. Then throw it into the said pot. If you want to preserve the flesh, the pieces must be somewhat thicker, but everything must be properly washed. Do not, though, throw away the pips and the bits but throw away the water and replace it with fresh, add a handful of salt and let it stand for a couple of days. Then change the water again and pour two or three fresh lots over the pieces and then a further one and let it stand for a whole day. Each morning pour fresh water over them and go on doing that for nine days. On the ninth day put the vessel on to the fire and at first let it simmer slowly, then bring it to the boil until you see that it is possible to stick a needle through the pieces. Take care, however, when you are boiling the flesh with the peel, that you remove them during the first boiling, otherwise they would be boiled too hard. When you have well and truly boiled everything and it has become a little stiff, take it off the fire and lift it out of the water with a perforated ladle on to a white cloth. Make sure that it is on the dry side, but treat it with care, so that it does not tear. When it has dried a little and cooled down, take as much sugar as you see fit. If there are two pounds of peel or pieces, use fine sugar and if you want to preserve them in the best possible manner, dissolve the sugar in water. There should not, however, be too much water, only as much as the quantity of sugar requires, and when it is ready, do not refine or clarify it, but allow it or the honey to reduce to a rather thick syrup. Whatever you do, do not burn it, for anyone who is not accustomed to doing this may easily burn it. Once it has reduced to a thick syrup, let it cool before putting it into the glass container with the peel. Leave it there until the following morning, when you will notice that the peel and the pieces of lemon are giving off a moisture on account of the sugar and that the sugar is therefore more like a watery soup. Then boil the sugar without the peel until it acquires the correct consistency for a syrup. Then cool it and put it back into the container with the peel and let it stay there for three days. When that time has elapsed, boil it again if necessary and deal with it as on the previous occasion, but you will have to wait until the end of the month to find out how it turned out. Note, however, that if you put it into a glass container, you must let it boil completely and then it will keep for a long time. If, however, you put it into an earthenware vessel, you should boil the sugar or honey somewhat more vigorously and leave more moisture in it, for no matter whether the vessel is glazed or not, the clay is constantly wearing away, which glass does not do. You can use this method with all other things you may wish to preserve with sugar. If you want to preserve bitter-orange or lime peel in sugar, then you must go about it as I have described for lemons. If, however, you want to preserve them in honey or boiled wine, you must do so in an altogether different way, as you will see when we come to that.

IVGLANS.

vuelfchnuß

❧ HOW TO PRESERVE PUMPKINS,

*which serve to cool internal fevers and have a
very pleasant taste.*

Take the ordinary long or round pumpkins, which are very hard and are gathered in autumn. They should have been cut or collected about a month beforehand, for they will then be all the better. Cut them into pieces – as many as you wish – and remove the hard rind, because that is not needed. Take as much of the thick and solid flesh as you are able and when you have cut up the pieces so that each is four fingers wide and five long, put them into a glazed earthenware vessel. Cover the bottom with salt and one of the pieces and crush the salt into a fine powder. When all the pieces are well salted, leave them standing for three or four days, until they become stiff, and the first piece will also attract the remaining moisture from the pumpkin pieces to itself, so that they will all the more readily take the sugar, thereby becoming stiffer and better-tasting. For all that, take care that they do not stink of salt, for if that were the case, they would be spoilt. When, therefore, the pieces have been in the salt for three days, remove them and wash them ten or twelve times or until they no longer taste of salt when you try them. Then boil them in very clean water. When they are partially saturated, drain it off, so that if any salt should have remained and not come out during the washing process, it would have been brought out by this short boiling. Then boil the pieces again in clean water until you can easily pierce them with a needle, and as soon as they are soft, use a perforated ladle to put them into cold water. Let them cool down in that, for it will make the flesh somewhat stiffer. When they have thus cooled, let them dry for a short while on a white cloth, for if you put the sugar on them too early you will not finish them for a very long time, for they have too much moisture in them. For that reason, when they are well and truly dry, dissolve an appropriate amount of good-quality sugar, according to the number of pieces – equal quantities of sugar and pieces. As usual allow the sugar to boil until it reaches the consistency of a syrup. When it cools down, put it in a vessel with the pumpkin pieces on top. Take a look at your efforts the following morning and boil the sugar once more without the pieces (for if you were to boil it with the pieces, which usually happens with things preserved in sugar or honey, they would become as hard as leather), until it has the correct consistency of a syrup. When it has cooled down, pour it over the pieces once more and continue doing this three or four times until you can see that the pieces are no longer giving off moisture, and are clean and clear when you hold them to the light. At that stage stop boiling the syrup. Now take some finely-powdered sugar and make a bed or base out of the said pieces and the sugar. Let them dry and then the pieces will have acquired a white coating of sugar and the flesh inside will be moist and taste excellent. These preserved pumpkins are very good to eat, although they are also useful as a cooling medicine and are really most delectable. They also serve to alleviate too much heat of the heart or liver.

PICEA PEREGRINA.

frembd oder welfch fiechte.

Conis antiqus.

Conis recentis magnitudo.

II.

❦ PRESERVING BITTER ORANGES IN SUGAR OR HONEY, *which are exceptionally delicious and good.*

Take some bitter oranges and cut them into four or six pieces, but at least four. Remove the pips or seeds, so that nothing remains except the peel, the flesh and the juice. Next take the rind or peel and let it steep in good clean water into which you have previously thrown a good heap of salt, so that it takes away the superfluous bitterness from the oranges. Let it stand thus for twenty-four hours and then drain it off. Pour another lot on and do the same every day for nine days. When these have passed, boil the peel in good well water and test with a needle to see if it will easily pass through a piece. When you notice that it does, remove the peel from the fire and use a strainer to put it into cold water. When the pieces have cooled, dry them a little on a white linen cloth and when you have done that, put them into a glass container or earthenware vessel and fill it with them. Next take two or three pounds of sugar, depending on whether the container is large or small, and if the sugar is of good quality it will not need cleaning or clarifying, so then dissolve it in the same quantity of water as the weight of the sugar. Afterwards let it simmer until it reaches the right form and consistency of a syrup. Do that once and then take it off the fire and let it cool. Put the rind or peel into it and allow the pieces to be well and truly saturated in the syrup. The following day boil it again as you think fit, let it cool and pour it into the container with the pieces of peel. Leave it there for three days and at the end of that time boil it up again as before. When you see that it is boiling, throw the rind or peel into the mixture and bring it back to the boil five or six times, but no more, lest they become too hard. Put everything back into its container and leave it there undisturbed for about a month. If you recognize or notice that it then needs boiling again, do so, but if not, leave it as it is. After everything has been well and truly boiled, if you wish you may add a small stick of cinammon and some ground cloves into it and it will become exceptionally exquisite. If, however, you wish to preserve bitter oranges in honey, take as many as you want, stir them in a preserving pan until it begins to bubble and when it has frothed well, let it stand until it has cooled. Then remove the froth with a skimmer and pour the honey on the peel, and then carry on as above and as described with the aforementioned sugar.

❦ HOW TO PRESERVE WALNUTS *or*

other fruits without honey or sugar which are preserved just as well, or perhaps a little worse than with sugar though better than with honey. However, where sugar or honey is not available, all kinds of things can be preserved by using this method.

I n all kinds of different places in the world one may encounter shortages and surpluses of things which nature has provided either for the sustenance of our life or for our pleasure and delight. Thus in one country there will be a considerable surplus of sugar and in another considerable supplies of honey, while sugar is very expensive. So, too, in other places where one can acquire neither sugar nor honey, the wonderful warmth and rays of the sun bring forth and sustain other fruits which satisfy our requirements and wishes. For example, those who have no wine prepare certain juices instead which closely resemble wine in taste, smell and beauty. Those, too, who have neither sugar nor honey, whose knowledge is too slight for them to do such things properly, they are able to use this recipe. So, by following it, you will be able to preserve all kinds of fruits which will not be lacking, either in taste or goodness, and will be worthy of no less esteem than if they had been preserved with sugar. It is true that they are not as pleasant as those done with sugar, but they are much pleasanter than those done with honey.

PLANTAGO MINOR.   III   spiſziger wegrich

❦ MAKING BOILED WINE, *which Marcus Varro calls* defrutum, *and how one preserves all kinds of things with it.*

During the time of the grape harvest take the must from an old vineyard and as many of the ripest grapes you can obtain. Put them into a large, wide cauldron and boil them well. As soon as it begins to form scum and boil, remove the scum completely and cleanly as long as it continues to appear, but always over a hot fire. Let it carry on boiling until it has reduced to a quarter of its volume and has become like a syrup. When it has boiled sufficiently, remove it from the fire, strain it through a fine cloth, a sieve or a bag through which flour is sieved – even strain the residue at the bottom – and put it into a glass container or a well-glazed earthenware vessel.

If, however, you want to preserve walnuts in boiled wine, take as many green nuts as you want, peel them thoroughly and steep them in water for nine days. Each day pour fresh water over them and at the end of this time boil them until they are soft and may easily be pierced with a needle. When they have been boiled sufficiently, take them off the fire and lay them on a dry white cloth and, when they are half-dry, put on to each walnut a small piece of a cinammon stick and insert about two cloves into each – the more you have, the better. When the nuts are covered with the small pieces of cinammon and cloves, fill a glass or earthenware container with them and pour the boiled wine over the nuts. Let them stand for three days and after that time drain off the wine and let it simmer in a preserving pan until it becomes like a scale when you coat the nuts with it, for if you have boiled it two or three times in this manner, the boiled wine, which Marcus Varro calls *defrutum*, has absorbed and consumed the moisture of the nut, but not so much that it does not immediately dry. If it were boiled too much, it would immediately crystallize and form a lot of blisters, even though it were in a glass container. In this way you can preserve all kinds of things with this boiled wine and it is also very good for many kinds of sauces which one uses daily with food. It can, however, be made only once a year. You should know, also, that if the must has been made for a whole or even half a day, it is of no use, because immediately it has been pressed from the grapes it must be placed in a kettle over the fire, otherwise its nature will alter and it will lose its taste, sweetness and loveliness and become sour like vinegar and an old decanted wine. That is why you should boil it as soon as it has been pressed and put into a glass container or a glazed one, as our forefathers used to do in the time of the Romans, before glazing was discovered. They used to put it into an earthenware jar which was sealed in the following manner.

Take a large or small earthenware jar (glazed or not), pitch, and a little tallow of the kind used for candles. Put the pitch and tallow inside and place the jar over the fire. Then take a stick and tie some flax on the end and wipe it around all over the inside until the jar is well and truly coated. Then boil the pitch and the tallow so that they fire evenly, but will not melt in the summer heat. Note that for a jar containing or holding twenty-five pounds, four ounces of pitch and one ounce of tallow will be sufficient to coat it all over. A jar coated internally with pitch can be used as you will for oil or boiled must. Do not worry that anything will seep out – not even nitric acid will. Not a drop of oil will leak out. In fact, from the outside it is not possible to say what is in the jar, whether it is oil or any other penetrating liquid. You will thus be able to preserve your boiled wine perfectly for a long time. Therefore if you wish to preserve something else or think it would be a

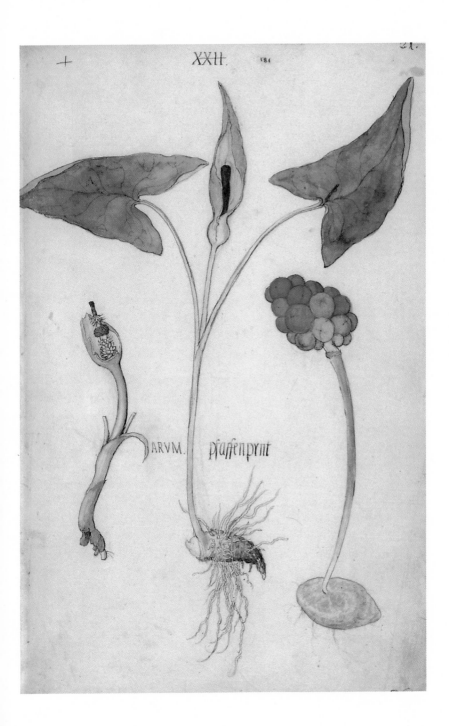

ARVM. pfaffenprnt

good idea to do so, you can do it with this wine just as well and bring it to a successful conclusion, apart from all the other useful things you may do with it during the course of the year. In some places in France it is boiled in such a manner that it becomes firm like quince jelly, it turns into grape salt, or is called that, and is merely used like salt in the kitchen. For the kind, however, which is not boiled to that extent but only so that it still remains soft, one uses the cleanest and purest must, containing neither pips nor anything else, which has come straight from the press.

HOW TO CLARIFY SUGAR *which has been kept in a chest and become blackened and unsightly, not only for preserving the items already mentioned but all kinds of other things.*

Take as much sugar as you want and dissolve it in water for as long as necessary. Put the container on to the fire and while the sugar is coming to the boil, put two measures, or one and a half or as much as three pounds of water into another vessel or preserving pan. Put into it the whites of two eggs and a little white vinegar – about three drachms. Then take a small, straight stick, about one foot in length, to the end of which you should tie some rushes, of the kind used to bind figs. Then beat the egg-whites in the water with the vinegar without stopping until it turns into a white froth. Remove this froth with the stick, throw it into the preserving pan containing the sugar and boil it steadily. When you see that the sugar is rising as it boils, add some more of the said froth and go on doing so as long as it lasts. When the sugar has percolated the froth and blackened it, remove the froth which is floating on top and throw it away and continue to remove it while it boils. After you have done that, take a white linen cloth, moisten it in cold water and carefully strain the liquid through it into another container and boil it until it reaches perfection, becoming as thick as syrup or even more boiled, as the lettuce stems themselves have a great deal of moisture, and then let it cool. When that has happened, pour it into the container with the lettuce, so that the stems are immersed in it, and leave it there for two days. After that boil the sugar without the lettuce, which should not be removed from the container. When the sugar has been thoroughly boiled, let it cool and pour it back over the lettuce. After six days boil the sugar again thoroughly, throw the lettuce stems in and let everything come to the boil two or three times, but no more. Then put everything back into the container prepared for it, leave it open until it has cooled, then cover it well and seal it properly. You will then have a thoroughly excellent confection which has a marvellous cooling effect in times of great and unbearable heat and if someone who is suffering from a three-day or persistent fever or any other unnatural excess of heat were to take some of it, he would feel exceptionally cheerful. Similarly, if someone suffers from considerable thirst at night, it soon gets rid of it and allows the sick person to sleep soundly.

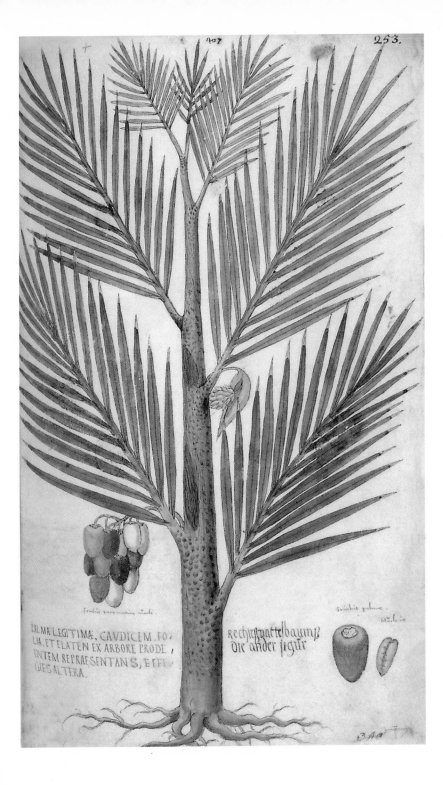

253.

❧ HOW TO PRESERVE BITTER CHERRIES *in the most delectable and exquisite manner so that, although the process may have been undertaken the previous year, they yet have the appearance of being prepared the very same day.*

Take about three pounds of the most beautiful and ripest bitter cherries you can obtain (but if they are not fresh, boil them until nothing remains after straining except the stones and skins). If you think that the stalks are too long, shorten them. Then take a pound and a half of sugar and dissolve it in three or four pounds of another bitter cherry brew or juice, making sure that you add the sugar immediately the juice has been extracted. Then put it over the fire and dissolve it only with the said juice. Let it boil as quickly as possible and remove any scum during the boiling. When you have done this to the best of your ability and see that the sugar has turned red and is thoroughly refined and purified, do not remove it from the fire but let it go on boiling and drop the bitter cherries into it. Stir them gently but continuously with a spatula until they are thoroughly cooked and foaming. Still do not take them off the fire until they are cooked right through, so that you do not have to put them on to the fire again. When you put a drop on a pewter plate and see that it does not run, then it is properly boiled, so pour it while still warm into small containers holding three or four ounces. You will then have beautiful red, whole bitter cherries with a most delectable taste which will keep for a long while. I, however, have been to many and varied places in the world and have learned and experienced this and that and how this one does a thing one way and another a different way, so that I should run out of paper were I to attempt to write everything down. I believe, however, that France and Italy excel in this matter, though from what I have seen they go about it in an odd way. So I have seen it made in Toulouse, Bordeaux and Rochelle and recently, while we are on the subject, also in Genoa, Languedoc, the whole of the Dauphiné and in the area round about Lyons, but I have never come across more beautiful and better ones than these. In Toulouse they boil them five or six times and several times in Bordeaux. Eventually, though, when they are five or six months old, some go rotten and bad and useless and others shrivel. If you want to preserve them properly you must use nothing except the juice of bitter cherries, as it increases their goodness, size and taste. For if a sick person takes just a single one, he will consider it as a balsam or other strengthening substance. After a lapse of a year they are as good as they were on the first day.

ISVM MAIVS   Groß garten erbeysen

❦ MAKING A TRANSPARENT JELLY FROM BITTER CHERRIES *which is as clear and red as a ruby and tastes extraordinarily nourishing, which will also keep extremely well for a very long time without the use of any ingredient apart from the fruit and which can easily be prepared on account of its excellence.*

T ake as many as you like of the most beautiful and ripest bitter cherries which you can obtain, remove the stalks and place the cherries in a sieve or bag used for sieving flour. Put an earthenware vessel underneath them – it must not be of copper, brass or pewter, otherwise the juice would be spoilt and lose its colour. Before doing that, however, you must have put as much well-pounded sugar as necessary in the container, depending on whether you want to make a lot or a little. If there were no sugar in the container when the juice fell into it, it would alter considerably and be of no use. When done in this way, the sugar absorbs the juice and acquires its colour and taste. Once the juice has been strained and nothing remains except the stones and the skins, heat up the fire and let it boil, while skimming it thoroughly with a skimmer. You must know, however, that if you want to make a beautiful, correct and proper bitter-cherry jelly, you should use as little sugar but as much juice as possible, so that it will keep for a long while. Boil it over a gentle coal fire, but make sure that the fire is under the centre of the preserving pan, so that it does not burn, and boil it in the appropriate manner. If you take a little out, either with a spatula or a silver spoon, and put it on a plate or pewter vessel, when it is ready the juice will stay put and not run in all directions. But take care that you do not boil it too much, for it is better that it is a little runny, rather than boiled too hard. If you want to keep it for a long time, dry the sugar beforehand. When the liquid has boiled, pour it into small, low, shallow bowls and let it cool. If, afterwards, you hold it up to the sun or your candle and look through it, it will be as red and beautiful as a ruby. If you take a little of it in your mouth it will have a marvellous, delectable taste, the like of which you will never have tried before in your life. If, however, the bitter cherries are not ripe, but still green, whether there are many of them or not, they will taste so bitter that they will ruin your teeth and instead of having a delectable confection it will be entirely unpalatable. The proper jelly, however, may be given to a prince or noble lord or also to someone with a severe fever or who does not feel well, and such a person will find that it is invigorating and exceptionally pleasant, without any harmful after-effects, and if you make it as I have described here, without doubt it will turn out excellent.

❦ ANOTHER METHOD OF MAKING *a transparent jelly from bitter cherries which is more delicate and expensive than the previous one and for use only by the nobility.*

Take two pounds of best-quality sugar, pound it coarsely and put it into a preserving pan. Next take six, seven or even eight pounds of bitter cherries, remove the stalks, squash them roughly with your clean hands and put them in the preserving pan with the sugar before placing it over the fire. Let it half boil, stirring it with a small wooden stick, and when it is saturated, strain it through a stiff, clean linen cloth, squeezing it a bit. Then put what you have strained into another preserving pan and boil it over a low fire. Always pay careful attention to whether it is ready, because it reduces a lot, so periodically take a little out with a spatula or silver spoon to see if it has boiled sufficiently. Be careful that the fire is not too fierce or vigorous, for otherwise it would boil over or catch on the bottom. You will be able to tell when it is ready because if you allow a drop to fall on a marble slab it should stay stiff in one place like a ball and not run to and fro. A similar thing will also happen if you let a drop fall on to a piece of pewter or the end of a knife and it looks like fine red wine. So when the juice has been boiled sufficiently, put it into small bowls or containers, as one does with quince jelly. When, however, these have cooled and stood for a while, you will have a type of dark jelly, of which it would be impossible to find a more beautiful, better or more excellent example. It is true that it is even more delicate and exquisite than the jelly made by the previous method, but both deserve esteem. If you were to travel throughout the whole world, you would get to know all kinds of different

AVRANTIA MALVS.

pomerantzenbaum

recipes and learn how to make them, either by observation or through the efforts or accounts of other people or would acquire the skill through long and constant practice, yet you would still not find one that is more famous or delectable. And if this small book should come into the hands of someone skilled in these matters, even if he is accustomed to speak ill of other people, he will truly not be able to find fault with it, for this is not only the best way and method of making these jellies, but also has all the other recipes contained in it. I feel it would be appropriate to mention at this point that I myself have made everything which I have described, or have had it made for me, mostly in my presence. It is true that amber was not always included in the oil described in the first book. Nevertheless, I myself have had all the confections described so far and those which are still to follow made for me in many and varied places and I have always been present. There are many people still alive who will bear witness to the truth of what I say. Yet there may perhaps be found some gossip who is not able to imitate me in this matter, but is accustomed to speak evil of people, and who might say that there is no great skill involved. I admit it, but at least I am the first to have concerned myself with the amount of material contained in the other book, to have written it down in our language and broken the ice. Not everyone can do this. There will be a lot of people who are most desirous of preserving all kinds of things and they will find ample instructions in the book.

❧ HOW TO MAKE GREEN GINGER

which, although it is called green, is in fact made from a ginger called Mecquin, as it comes from Mecca, where Muhammad is buried.

Take some white ginger or the kind from Mecca (for that is better) and let it steep for three days in hot water, adding fresh water to it each day. Then take a very sharp lye made from vine ashes and boil the ginger in it for the first time. Throw that water away, pour some more over it and test to see if it has lost its sharpness. For if it is not boiled repeatedly it will not lose its sharpness, but easily becomes soft. So when it has been boiled repeatedly in the lye and the latter has absorbed the sharpness of the ginger, take it out and soak it in fresh water. Wash it well, but carefully, so that you do not bruise it. When it has been steeped for three or four days and you have given it fresh water each day, so that it loses the taste of the lye, then strain it into clean water with which a little honey has been mixed and take care that it is on the stiff side, rather than being too soft. Drain this water off and test again to see if it tastes of the lye or has any sharpness which is too noticeable. If you can detect that there is something still present, boil it for as long as it takes to acquire a pleasant taste. Then remove it from the fire and dry it on a white cloth. When it is dry, put it in a well-glazed earthenware vessel and turn it upside-down, so that the water runs out. Then take as much honey as you want (for it must be preserved only in honey, not sugar) and put it into a preserving pan. Boil it two or three times, take it off the fire, let it cool and when it has done so, whisk it with a skimmer until there is nothing except froth. Then put the cold and well-whisked honey into the container with the

XXIX

369.

VITIS VINIFERA.

weinreb.

ginger, filling it up with honey. Let it stand for two or three days and if at the end of that time you notice that the honey has been boiled too quickly and is too runny, empty everything out and boil it carefully. Boil the ginger no more than two or three times and then replace it in its container and seal it well. You should note, however, that this preserved ginger has a disadvantage and an advantage, and if you assess both correctly, you will find that the disadvantage is outweighed. It is that because of being boiled in the lye the ginger loses its sharpness, which is strong like a spice. If, however, that attribute were to be preserved, it would be so sharp and strong that no one would like it or be able to try it, no matter how it had been preserved. The lye is used for no other reason than to remove the sharpness and to absorb it, thereby bringing about the loss, for anyone who wanted to enjoy it only with its sharpness, his head would be set on fire. The advantage is this: it is a small spice, which is hard and heavy as it is soaked in honey, and a preserved root or small piece of ginger, which otherwise would not be heavier than one and a half drachms, weighs as much as an ounce. As far as the potency and effect of green ginger are concerned, it is primarily of use for women who are unable to have children because of abdominal frigidity, or in cases of chilled stomach and for elderly people whose natural heat has almost been extinguished. It is, however, of much greater benefit to those impotent or too weak in the work of love, who may wish to use it. If you put it into a fine sugar syrup it will taste all the better, but not as hot.

❦ HOW TO OBTAIN GINGER WATER,
which reduces to a useful powder and produces an excellent spiced wine.

T ake some ginger and boil it in clean water until it becomes soft. Make sure that there is enough water, so that it can absorb the sharpness of the ginger better, which you would find very sharp and strong were you to try it. Remove the water and put it to one side and boil the ginger in another lot, in the same way as you did the first time. When you see that the ginger has been well cooked, remove it and squeeze it firmly, but do not crush it. When all the water has been squeezed out and has acquired the sharpness of the ginger, take it and boil it in a large kettle until the moisture has almost entirely evaporated and allow the remainder to dry out in an earthenware pot. If you test it, you will taste that it has drawn all the sharpness of the ginger into itself and if you were to put a little into an hippocras, it would give it the kind of kick and bite which are not to be despised. It may also be used in a salve made from spices. I have also had this water, which acquires the sharpness of ginger, prepared for Franciscus Berardus, who purchased it as being an entirely new spice.

❦ PRESERVING THE ROOTS OF FIELD ERYNGOS AND WELTED THISTLES IN SUGAR, *which are not only entirely comparable in strength and goodness to green ginger but also have a sweeter taste.*

Take the largest field eryngo or welted-thistle roots you can acquire; they should have been gathered in winter, for that is the time when all the strength is in the roots. Peel these with a good sharp knife and when you have removed the fine outer skin, cut the roots up into small pieces. Take the smoothest ones, which are about half a finger in length, but make sure that you do not remove the flesh, otherwise you would harm yourself and the confection. When you have cleaned these roots properly, boil them in water and throw two or three cloves of crushed ginger in with them. Boil the roots until they become soft. When they are, remove them from the fire and let them dry off on a small white linen cloth, before putting them into an earthenware pot or container. Then take as much sugar as you consider necessary, dissolve it in water and boil it until it becomes like syrup. Next take two ounces of best ginger and an ounce of white pepper. Pulverize them, then take the field eryngo roots and put everything into an earthenware pot, taking care to see that it is not damp. Sprinkle the powder over it and when you have done so, put it back into its pot or container, adding the sugar syrup. After three or four days, when the syrup has absorbed some of the moisture from the roots, if they have still not been sufficiently cooked, do not boil them again but place them in the sun or in a room for a few days, so that this undesirable moisture evaporates, for

LACTVCA SYLVESTRIS.

wilder lattich.

III.

if you were to boil the roots again, the powder would be dissipated and all the strength would be lost in the boiling. You have here a recipe for green ginger, which is hardly distinguishable from the proper kind, has an attractive taste, is more potent than the genuine one and does not require any more effort or expense to make.

❦ HOW TO PRESERVE GREEN, UNRIPE ALMONDS IN SUGAR

Take as many as you want of fresh almonds which are still tender and green. Peel them as carefully as you are able, making sure that the leaves are there as well. When you have peeled them, boil them in clean water until they become soft. When they have boiled as much as is necessary, take them off the fire and remove them from the hot water. Put them into cold water to stiffen up again somewhat and then dry them well on a clean white cloth. When that has been done, put them into a container and turn it upside-down, so that if there is too much moisture present it will run out. Then take as much sugar as you have almonds or, if you have got two pounds of almonds, then after they have boiled take one and a half pounds of sugar; the sugar should be dissolved in three small quarts of good well water. If your sugar is of good quality you will not need to clarify it, so boil it until it has the consistency of a syrup. You can tell when that stage has been reached if, when you put a drop on to a marble slab, it stays as such, does not run and no more steam rises from it. When you see that the sugar has boiled as it should, take it off the fire and let it cool right down. Then put it into the container with the almonds and let it stay there for two days. At the end of that time boil it up to a syrup again and, when it has cooled, pour it back over the almonds. Leave it there for four or five days, and after that time boil it up to a syrup again and when it has cooled, put it back into the container. Do, however, take care not to boil the almonds together with the sugar, for were that to happen, the green leaves, which are fragile and delicate, would shrivel up in the first boiling and be spoilt. That is why you should boil the sugar by itself

MALVS ARMENIACA.

Amarillen baum

II.

and not include the almonds, for otherwise you would make a fine, praiseworthy and tasteful confection, but not a delicate one. Some people want to change the character of the almonds and make them seem commonplace. They do so by putting a piece of cinnamon and one or two cloves on each, with the aim of making the confection smell more pleasant and attractive. One can, however, make them without cinnamon and cloves or with both, just as anyone wishes. If they are preserved with spices, it is better to classify them as delicious foods which may be enjoyed daily, rather than as medicine. Even if they are not often used in this manner, except when they have been preserved with their shells, which are a bit acid, they can be given for cases of slight fever, which does not occur very often. They are far more frequently enjoyed for pleasure, just like other confections which are made and prepared on a daily basis in one way or another, according to the desires and wishes of different people, one of whom desires to have them prepared one way and another in a different way. They may be preserved properly, however, only in sugar, honey or boiled wine. Someone wishing to please himself, though, can preserve them in boiled wine, for that way they taste fine and delicious.

❦ HOW TO MAKE SUPERB QUINCE
JELLY, *which may be kept for a long time and is fit to be set before a king.*

Take as many quinces as you want – but they must be ripe and a beautiful yellow colour. Cut them up into pieces, but do not peel them (for those who do peel them do not know what they are doing, because the rind or peel enhances the smell). Each quince should be divided into five or six segments and the seeds should be removed, because they are better without them. When you have cut them up, place them in a basin with water, for otherwise they will turn black. Then boil them in a good amount of water until they turn to pulp. When they have boiled thoroughly, strain the liquid through a thick linen cloth and squeeze it as tightly as you can. If you have six pounds or three measures of liquid, add one and a half pounds of Madeira sugar to it, before boiling it over a gentle coal fire until you see that it has boiled sufficiently and reduced in volume. Then damp the fire down somewhat, so that the liquid does not catch, which would have a very adverse effect upon the colour of the juice. If you want to know whether it has boiled sufficiently, take a spatula or silver spoon and put a little on a plate and when it has cooled, if you see that it does not run, but has gelled and does not disintegrate, then it is ready. Take it off the fire, remove the scum and pour the liquid into small containers or bowls, of whatever shape you wish, which is easily done and is good to behold. The colour is so clear that it looks like an oriental ruby. The taste of the jelly is no less precious and it may be given to sick and healthy alike.

❦ ANOTHER METHOD OF MAKING A
clear quince jelly, which is even more attractive
and concentrated, yet similar in taste. It is
true that it is more expensive, but a person
who requires it for princes and members of the
nobility need make no other than this one, for it
surpasses all others. One should, however, not
be too niggardly as far as this is concerned, but
much rather err on the generous side.

Take twelve or fourteen quinces, peel them very carefully and thinly, cut each into eight or ten segments and remove all traces of the seeds. When you have done that, boil them in a good quantity of water and when they have almost boiled, add three or four pounds of fine sugar and let them carry on boiling. Add more water to enable them to boil better. When the quinces are almost cooked, strain them through a clean white linen cloth, but do not squeeze it. Boil the strained liquid in a preserving pan over a low coal fire and when you consider that it has boiled sufficiently, test it frequently, using a silver spoon or clean spatula, to see if it is ready and has gelled properly. If, when you put a little on a piece of pewter or a plate, you see that it is firm, remove it from the fire and later boil it up thoroughly once more, for although it is already sticky and viscous, that will do it no harm, for it will soon become firm and acquire a lovely appearance and it will be possible to cut it like calves-foot jelly. Then put it in caskets, boxes or glass bowls and add some coats of arms or mottoes of noble lords, as you see fit, so that they may be clearly seen. Many people,

Langer dicker roter, vnd kc/t,
brauner calecutischer pfeffer.

AESICON LONGVM CRASSVM
RVBRVM, ET SPADICEV.

however, use only the viscous matter from around the quince seeds and try to thicken it, but are unable to do so, for the flesh has its own characteristics and interacts with the seeds and they are not therefore needed. Many people also want to give it colour with red sandalwood or brazilwood mixed with rose-water, but you do not need either sandalwood or brazilwood, since it will turn a beautiful red like scarlet or an oriental ruby as soon as it has properly boiled and thickened. It has, however, frequently happened that when someone is through with such foolish work it has turned black, caught and the juice has been well and truly ruined. But no one does that, except inexperienced people who are not used to dealing with such matters or are not skilled in them. Therefore if you want to make this jelly properly, so that it could be offered to a king, do not use anything except sugar and quinces. It is true that it will not be as good as that made by the first method, for there will be a lot of sugar left in the quince pieces, but as far as excellence and beauty are concerned, it truly surpasses all other jellies made anywhere else in the world. And so that you can see what I say is true, I call upon those who understand such matters and have often prepared them. How they were also prepared for Francis, the first of this name of blessed memory, King of France, and for Cardinal de Clarmont, who was also a legate at Avignon, in a manner such as had never been seen before. The Grand Master of Rhodes was also honoured with this jelly in the Year of Christ our Redeemer 1526, when he rode through Avignon. And in the same year in that most excellent and renowned city of Lyons he was honoured with that name even by the women.

❦ HOW TO PRESERVE LIMES *and bitter oranges while they are small and still green, producing a very pleasant and tasty confection which one can use as one wishes.*

Take as many tender, green bitter oranges and limes as you will, which have no pips or seeds, together with some small shoots or tender buds, which a tree produces each year when it acquires leaves. Heat up the limes and bitter oranges in good well water and do the same with the small shoots for four days. Then boil them in another lot of water. Take care, though, to pour fresh water over them each day. After the first boiling, throw in a handful of salt, so that in case they were still bitter, they would lose this through the salt and become more pleasant. When they are well boiled, that is to say thoroughly cooked, take them carefully off the fire and put them into cold water to cool. Take care, however, not to boil the shoots at the same time as the fruit, because they are tender and could not stand such boiling, but might even go bad because of it, but put them in only at the end when everything has almost been cooked as it should be. When everything has cooled down, lift it out and let it drain well, before putting it into a glass container or well-glazed vessel. Then take as much sugar as the bitter oranges require, dissolve it and boil it for the first time until it acquires the consistency of a syrup. When that has happened, take it off the fire and let it cool down, before putting the bitter oranges, the young shoots and the limes into it. Do make sure that the sugar boils to a syrup. Then cover the top of the container, put a parchment over it and tie it down. After two days strain the sugar off into a preserving pan and boil it until it acquires its previous consistency, that is until

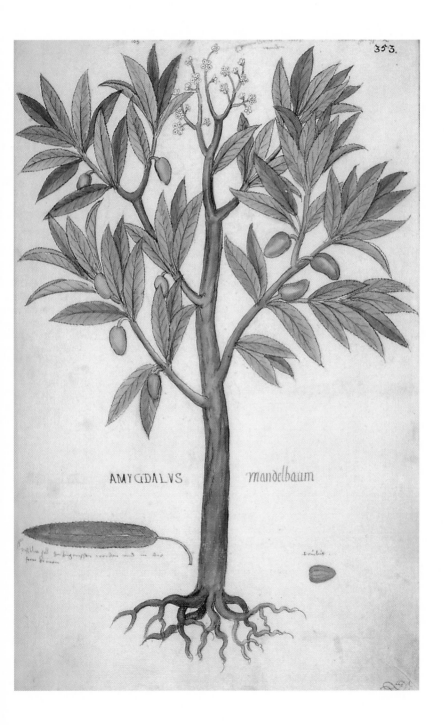

353.

AMYGDALVS   mandelbaum

it turns to a syrup. Let it cool down and put the fruit and shoots back into it. Leave them in the syrup for about five or six days, but check each day and then heat it up again as before, that is without the fruit. This last time, however, make sure that the sugar does not boil, otherwise the bitter orange and lime skins would become as hard as leather. When it is completely cold, pour the sugar over the fruit, because it does not need to be boiled again, and when the whole composition is ready, put it into a shallow earthenware vessel which is no more than two crossed fingers in depth, so that one can see it properly and when it is taken out it does not break in pieces, as happens with pots from Valencia or Spain or those made from Sicilian clay – or put it into another vessel which you think will be suitable. You should, however, be aware that you can preserve the fruit just as well in honey or boiled wine as in sugar. To tell the whole truth, however, it is not only this confection which is preserved more excellently in sugar but all others, too, whatever they are called. For jelly preserved with sugar is much more exquisite and delicate than that preserved with honey, which is a coarse and boorish substance, but really to be despised is the one preserved with boiled wine, although some people do prefer it to that preserved in honey. If I am to tell the truth, however, it is certain and there is no doubt about it that sugar is best for preserving jelly, because it will keep for a longer time. However, anyone can do as he likes in such matters, but as far as I am concerned, I award the honours to items preserved in sugar.

❦ HOW TO PRESERVE QUARTERED QUINCES IN ONE DAY, *which can be kept for an exceptionally long time and have an extremely pleasant taste and may be used in two different ways, namely for giving substance to dishes and for eliminating unnatural decomposition of the food or also for eating at any hour.*

Take some of the ripest and yellowest quinces which you can obtain. Cut each up into four pieces or, if you think that they would look ugly, cut them up into six or eight or as many pieces as you want and think would be suitable. Peel them thoroughly, making sure that none of the peel is left, nor any of the seeds, cores or kernels. When you have cleaned them as well as you can, boil them in as much water as is necessary until they are cooked, which you can tell if you stick a needle into them and it goes through easily. When you see that they are sufficiently cooked – better overdone than underdone – take as much sugar as the quantity of quinces requires and boil both together. If there is not enough water, pour some more in, for the more watery the sugar is, the more easily the quinces will assimilate it. If there is a shortage of water or it requires it and the sugar is boiled too rapidly, the quinces will not be cooked properly and only on the surface and the insides will still remain white. For that reason boil everything as necessary over a low coal fire until it comes to perfection, which you will be able to recognize when you let a drop or two fall on to a pewter plate. If it runs, then let it boil a bit more, for since the quinces are naturally somewhat moist, this moistness dissipates only slowly to resume its natural form. It is, however, true that when they are properly cooked they are so tender that one can hardly cut them with a knife. Then three, five or six days later, but no more, cut them like brawn and when you have done that and they have been cooked as I told you, put them into flat or wide boxes or containers and do not take them out until you want to eat them. You will frequently find among them a slice which will taste as good as balsam. Before you put them into the box you can put a little cinnamon or two or three cloves on each piece. Or if you want to improve upon that, grind the cinnamon and cloves to a fine powder and sprinkle that on them – use as much as is necessary. Anyone who wishes to make the recipe differently is at liberty to do so. This, however, is the best and most useful way, for anyone wishing to preserve them like other fruits would have to boil the sugar for a day, but not the other ingredients, which would take a great deal of time and they would still not be as good. They can also be preserved exquisitely in boiled wine in the following manner.

MALVS CYDONIA. kuttenbom.

❦ PRESERVING QUINCES INDIVIDUALLY IN BOILED WINE, *which are almost indistinguishable from those preserved in sugar. The process must, however, be carried out at the time of the wine harvest, then they will remain firm and usable for a year or two. The liquid in which they have been preserved remains excellent throughout the year and may be used for an embrocation or sauce.*

Take about twenty quinces, quarter each one, peel the pieces and clean them carefully, removing the skin, core, kernel and seeds. After you have cleaned them thoroughly, boil them in a kettle with must which has been pressed the same day from good ripe grapes, not green or sour ones. As soon as you have put the must into the kettle and it has boiled for the first time, remove the scum carefully and then immediately, without any hesitation, put all the quince pieces into the kettle and let them boil until the must has almost entirely evaporated – from every ten tankards of must hardly three will remain. If you want to know, however, when they have cooked sufficiently, take a piece, put it on a plate and cut it through the middle. It should then be neither white nor bitter, but sweet, tender and of good texture. Then remove it from the fire and put everything into a large earthenware pot. You will then have a confection which is as red as hyacinths and sweet as sugar and if you give someone a piece to taste, he will not be able to tell whether it was preserved in sugar or not, for it has neither the taste nor the smell of honey. Cover the pot well. When the quinces are thoroughly cooked, take a piece out with a skimmer, put it on a plate or in a dish and put a little cinnamon and some cloves on each piece. If you want to make it even better, strain the boiled wine or must from the quince pieces and keep it separately, for it is useful for a number of ordinary things and, if necessary, you can use it in place of sugar, but do not mix it with water and drink it, for sugar is of a moderate nature, but boiled wine is fiery. Otherwise they are just the same. Indeed if you keep the must for a year, it will candy like sugar. It is true that sugar is white; the boiled wine, however, is the colour of candied honey.

CARYOPHYLLVM   Rramernegelin

❧ HOW TO PRESERVE THE PEEL OR RIND OF THE ROOTS OF THE LARGE BLUE ALKANET IN SUGAR. *It strengthens the heart, protects a person from consumption and dropsy, makes him cheerful and happy, drives away all melancholy, rejuvenates people, slows down the ageing process, imparts a healthy colour to the face, keeps a person in good health and stops him from getting angry.*

In the month of Christ's birth take the peel or rind of the roots of the large blue alkanet – that being the time when the plants have almost no leaves (for if you were to gather them at the time when they have a lot and are growing, they would be of no use, because then all their strength is in the stems and the leaves). When you have got the roots, pick out the largest ones and remove only the rind or peel. Wash the pieces as well as you can but try not to scrape them. Cut them into wide strips, as wide as the rind or peel itself, but of medium length. When you have washed and cleaned them thoroughly, boil them in a good measure of peaty water. Once that has been done properly and in the appropriate manner, as is the case with other confections, remove the roots with a ladle and place them in a wide container which is two crossed fingers in depth. Do not, however, throw away the water in which they were boiled, for it contains a part of the plants' strength. For this reason take as much sugar as is necessary and dissolve it in the said broth, so that it becomes soft, and then boil it to the proper consistency of a syrup. If you notice that the sugar turns black in the said water and the syrup therefore looks unsightly, clarify it, or if you think it is all right, leave it. It is true that if the sugar is not dissolved in it, it will not be as potent. Therefore let it boil until it attains the consistency of a well-boiled syrup and, when that has happened, let it cool properly. Then pour it over the rind or peel and let the pieces steep in it for twenty-four hours. Then remove the syrup, boil it again and this time remove the scum, as you would from a poor syrup. When it has boiled, remove it from the fire very carefully and let it cool. When it is perfectly cool, pour it over the rind or peel again and leave it there for two or three days. If, when you look at it after the stated deadline, you consider that it should be boiled again, do so, but take care not to make the sugar too hot or to boil the peel in with it just a little, for the pieces would become as hard as tanned leather, so watch out. When you consider that you have done everything that you should, put the confection into small, shallow pots, so that you can remove it easily. That way you can see it all the better and use it more conveniently.

PRESERVING MUSCADEL OR SIMILAR PEARS IN SUGAR

Take as many of the best and smallest muscadel or similar pears suitable for preserving in sugar as you will and peel them as thinly as you possibly can. If the stalks are too long, cut a little off them, although it is better that they should be too long rather than too short, because it is then easier to get hold of them. When you have peeled them, put them into fresh water, so that they do not turn black. When you have done all that, put them into some well water, or other good water, the best that you can obtain, and boil them sufficiently, that is until you are able to stick a needle through them. When they are cooked, take them out with a ladle and let them cool in clean water. Then place them on a delicate, white and very clean linen cloth and let them dry of their own accord. When they have done so, put them into a well-glazed earthenware vessel or into glass bowls. Turn these upside-down, so that if a little water is still remaining it can drip out all the easier. Then take as much sugar as a glance tells you is necessary, dissolve it in water and, if it requires it, clarify it after it has dissolved; but if the sugar comes from Madeira you need not clarify it, since it is normally very white. To clarify it, put soft earth under a special vessel which has a point with a small hole, through which the sediment and all the moisture from the sugar trickles. What remains on top is the cleanest available. When the separating vessel begins to dry out, cover it with dried loam or lime, which absorbs moisture. Then take the clarified sugar from the layer which is ready and boil it until it is not only as thick as syrup but even thicker. When you have done that, let it cool a little before pouring it over the pears. If you think that the pears have been cooked too

PYRVS ARBOR   Byrnbom.

much, put a little warm sugar over them, so that they do not go off. And when the sugar has been boiled like a syrup and has been over the pears for two days, boil it up again like a syrup and when it is completely cold, pour it back into the vessel with the pears. Let it stay there for four days and then put the sugar into a preserving pan, but the pears into a dish and put a little cinnamon and one or two cloves on to each pear. When you have done that, put the pears back into their container and boil the sugar to a syrup once more. Once it has thus boiled, pour it back over the pears and seal the pot well. You will then have an excellent confection, one which is fit to present to a prince.

HOW TO MAKE AN ATTRACTIVE CANDIED SUGAR

Take about nine pounds of the most beautiful and whitest sugar (for a beautiful work is created from something beautiful, just as something bad comes from something bad or ugly) and dissolve it in an appropriate amount of water. If you do not consider that the sugar is sufficiently beautiful, clarify it until it has no more sediment. When you have done that, dissolve it completely and boil it again until it acquires the consistency of a syrup. It is better to overboil, rather than underboil it, for then it would candy to a salt. As soon as it is boiled, take an unglazed earthenware pot which has been specially made for the purpose and put a small pine twig, a reed or a small rod into it, so that the sugar may candy in the middle. When you have inserted your chosen rod, then pour the hot sugar into the pot, put the lid on it and seal it roughly with lime, merely in order to keep the heat inside for longer, and immediately bury it under some warm manure, be it in a public or a private place. If you think that the manure is not hot enough, pour some hot water over it and see that there is a good pile of it, so that the pot may stand in the middle – so cover it up well and leave it for nine days and nights. At the end of that time take it out of the dung heap, open the pot and pour out the syrup which has not yet candied and you will see that of the nine pounds of sugar, about five or six pounds will have candied. When you have properly drained the syrup out of the pot, get some good hot water and wash it out two or three times, so that it does not become affected by the syrup adhering to it. Add this water to the syrup and if you want to make this confection you must do it this way and not another way. You can make it another way, but that will cost at least as

OLEA SATI·
CVM MAIORIB:
CTIBVS

VA ALTERA
FOLIIS, ET FRV·

Der ander zam olbaum
II

OLEA SATIVA PRIMA CVM
MINORIBVS TVM FOLIIS, TVM
FRVCTIBVS

Der erst zam olbaum

I

much. You should also know that if the sugar stays under the manure for longer than nine days and the manure were hot, it would not candy, for the steam from the manure contains moisture, which penetrates everything, so the sugar would need an even longer time to candy. If you want all or most of the sugar to candy, boil it up to a syrup, take care that the pot has not been fired at too high a temperature and has not been washed just before you put the sugar into it or touched by any other water, so that there is no moisture in it, except that of the sugar. For this reason such pots must be made specially for this purpose. For if you want to take the candied sugar out in one piece, you must place it over a low coal fire, shake it a bit until you feel the sugar is moving and then break the pot and remove the candied sugar. Even if you are making less than eight or nine pounds you can, however, prepare all kinds of things with it. It is a lie, however, what some idle fellows say, namely that beautiful candied sugar can be made from filthy, coarse sugar. *Quia non ex musico, non fit musicus*. If, however, you wish to say that something beautiful can be made from a sugar which is not beautiful, I will tell you how it is done. Take a suitable amount of well-refined sugar which has not been boiled as hard as syrup and put it into a large earthenware pot. Make a hole at the bottom of this, according to the quantity of the sugar, and leave it there for four or five days. Allow half or somewhat more of the syrup to seep through the hole in the bottom. What is left will then be very beautiful, for sugar acts differently from honey, for the best sugar rises to the top, as is the case with oil. The best honey, however, stays at the bottom. Thus it is possible from a dirty sugar to make a very beautiful candied sugar, which tastes just as good. This then is how to make candied sugar, as it is also prepared in Genoa and Venice. Here at home, however, I have had it made from pressed olives, which was exceptionally good and very much like that which is brought from Venice.

❦ HOW TO MAKE A CONFECTION
FROM PINE-NUT KERNELS

Take as many well-cleaned and carefully shelled pine-nut kernels as you will, dry them or toast them a little. Or take them whole with their skins and shells and put them in a basket. Hang this over the hearth near the fire and leave it there for three days. Thus the heat from the fire will slowly penetrate them and dry them. Then take them out and clean them thoroughly. Next take two and a half pounds of nuts, being careful to keep them close at hand. Then take some of the most beautiful and best Madeira sugar, dissolve sufficient of it in rose-water and boil it until it attains the consistency of a jelly. If it is winter or a time when there is a lot of moisture in the air, boil it a bit longer, but if it is summer, then let it just simmer. This is when it does not boil over or bubble when it boils, which is a sign that the moisture had been evaporated; but to be brief, when it has boiled to the consistency of a jelly, as I have said, take the preserving pan off the fire and put it somewhere where the liquid can dry off and become firm. Then give it a good stir with a piece of wood and beat it continuously until it turns white. When it begins to cool down a little, add the white of a whole or half an egg and beat it well again. Next place it over the coals, in order to allow the moisture from the egg-white to stiffen, and when you see that it is properly white and like the first lot you boiled, take the dried, well-cleaned pine-nut kernels and put them into the sugar. Stir them with the wood so that they are thoroughly mixed with the sugar – this should still be done over the coal fire, so that the mixture does not cool too quickly. Then take a wide wooden knife, like the ones used by shoemakers, and cut the mixture into pieces, each weighing about an ounce and a half, but not more than

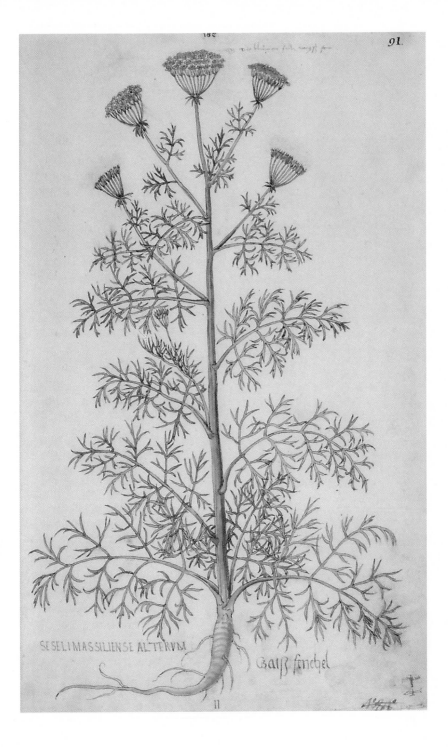

SESELI MASSILIENSE ALTERVM

Gaiß fenchel

two, which would not be good, and spread them carefully on to some paper until they have properly cooled, at which stage put a little gold leaf on to them and your confection is ready. If, however, it is not possible to obtain pine-nut kernels anywhere, use peeled almonds instead, dividing them either into two parts or three and mixing them with the sugar to make this confection. And if there are too few pine-nut kernels, you can replace them with pieces of almonds, for the latter are not dissimilar to the former in taste and potency. You can also use fennel which is flowering or in seed, which is kept in houses and used during the wine harvest. When your sugar has almost completely boiled and is hot and white with everything mixed in it or scattered over it, it looks like manna or snow and is so beautiful and lovely.

❦ HOW TO MAKE MARZIPAN

Take a pound of sweet, finely peeled almonds and pound them thoroughly in a marble mortar with half a pound of Madeira sugar. When you have ground everything well together, add a little rose-water, so that they do not deteriorate. Then make the mixture into small round rolls or cakes, put these on thin biscuits or wafers and bake them in an oven. When they are half-cooked or baked, take some powdered sugar, beat into it some egg-white and a little bitter-orange juice, but make sure that it is beautiful and soft. When the little cakes are almost baked, lift them out of the oven, apply a little sugar to them with a feather and put them back in the oven, to colour up. When they have baked you will find that they have a delicate and excellent taste. If you take too much sugar, however, the mixture will become doughy and very unlovely and unpleasant to eat. If you want to bake them at home, as often as you wish and with the minimum of effort, heat up an iron shovel, of the kind you use on the hearth, and place the small cakes or rolls on a bench or table. Then take the glowing shovel and pass it over the cakes for as long as it take for them to start to colour up, but take care not to touch them with it. When they have baked on one side, turn them over and bake them until they are ready. When this stage has been reached they will have acquired their colour, as was mentioned before. When made this way they are better than if they had been baked in an oven, because they cannot burn. Usually, however, they are not prepared in this manner, except in an emergency, but are more often baked. These small cakes were called marzipan by Hermolad Barbarus; they may be used as medicine but are very nice to eat at any time. It may well be that some people will mock me for describing such

ROSA DOMESTICA EX RVBRO
DILVTA

zam leibfarb rofen.

a simple thing, which any apothecary can make. You should know, however, that I do this much more on behalf of the ordinary man and ordinary woman, who are very pleased to learn new things, and really on behalf of virtually everyone and, lastly, because although many apothecaries are able to do a great number of things, they nevertheless do not know about this. Take note, however, that if you want to make a delightful, fresh and delectable little cake, bake it when the almonds are still fresh and have only recently been picked from the trees. If you attempt to make them any other way you will find a great difference in their taste and goodness.

❦ HOW TO MAKE PENIDE SUGAR,

which, although the method was described long ago by a learned Arab called Bulcasis, is nevertheless the correct and complete method and way of preparing the same.

Take some sugar of reasonably good quality, such as is kept in chests, and dissolve it in sufficient water, namely three small quarts. Boil it and strain it very carefully, so that there are no bits or pieces of cane straw in it, such as usually stick to it. Put the strained sugar back into the preserving pan and give it a final boil. When you see that it has boiled to a thick liquid, damp down the fire somewhat and take a spindle and put it in a glass of water. When you want to see if the sugar has boiled sufficiently, dunk the spindle in it and immediately put it back into the glass of water to cool it. Then put it in your mouth to taste it. If your teeth tell you that the sugar is very sticky, then it has not been boiled enough. For this reason you must keep testing it, because if you were to fail to do so, it would burn and be spoilt. Therefore keep trying with the spindle and dunk it in the boiling sugar and put it straight into the glass, waving it to and fro to cool it. Test it again with your teeth and if it breaks like glass, remove it from the fire at once. Skim it a little, but not for long. Then immediately pour it on to a marble slab coated with a little oil, but not enough to taint it. If you have not got a marble slab, pour it on to a table of walnut wood, which retains the heat well. When you have done that and everything is spread out, make the sugar into a heap or a lump again. Once it is malleable, take it, hot as it is (which one can hardly bear to do), and attach it to an iron hook, specially made for the purpose. Pull it apart as far as you can, but try not to be affected by the heat as you pull, and do not coat your hands with anything except starch. Take care to begin pulling it with the very tips of your fingers and then use the whole fist, then it will remain stuck to your hands and will pull from the hook – once you pull a little, it will stretch out and extend as long as you want. If you notice that it is not beautiful and white as you pull it, then pull it a bit more and put a warming pan underneath the hook and when one person has to let go, another must take it. Take care not to burn your hands, for the sugar can get extremely hot and remain so for some time. When you see that it has whitened, wind it or spin it thickly or thinly and daintily, as you will. Spread out some sheets of thin paper and sprinkle them with some fine starch. If, when you have pulled the sugar and wound it, you would like it to harden within the hour, put it in a wide box above the fireplace or somewhere else where it can stay in the warm and within half an hour it will turn to a loaf. Or you can place the box in an empty barrel, together with a warming pan, so that it is kept really warm. Make sure, however, that the barrel is properly covered and it will have set in half an hour. One cannot, however, make more than two, or at most two and a half, pounds at the same time. Whatever you do, add nothing to it, neither honey nor oil, as some ignorant fools do, for it only turns the sugar black and that is the reason why it smells bad and if it is kept for some time it will turn red and mouldy and then black as well. So if you want to make it exceptionally beautifully and in the proper manner, you need nothing except sugar from a chest or some that is already a loaf, but the latter is always stiffer at the point than at the bottom. You should be aware that if you want to use such sugar you can use it to make a fine penide sugar, but it is not as easy as it is with sugar from chests, for the latter's delicate nature makes it easier to pull

munch rhabarbarum.

and the more it is pulled, the whiter it becomes. Bulcasis, on the other hand, is of the opinion that for every pound of sugar you should use one ounce of honey. However, without wishing to speak ill of him, there are those who have sought to emulate him in this matter and have made an ugly and unpleasant penide sugar, just like the others, who, when they had almost finished, added sweet almond oil to it, so that it later went mouldy. The result was that instead of alleviating the pain of a sore throat, it made it burn far worse. If you really want to have proper penide sugar, make it according to the above description.

❦ MAKING PURGING ROSE-WATER
which, if you take an ounce of it, will produce a wonderful effect without any other ingredient. Pregnant women may be given it during their first and last months and it may be taken at any age and at any time without the slightest danger.

Take 900 or almost 1,000 of the most beautiful flesh-coloured roses, the buds of which are half-open and which still have leaves. When you have carefully plucked off the leaves and cleaned the buds in the best possible manner, rub the buds between your hands, so that in case one were still whole, it would open and the hot water would be able to penetrate it all the better. Then put the roses into a large glazed earthenware pitcher and boil them sufficiently in well water. Add additional boiling water and stir the roses well with a piece of wood or a stirring spoon, so that they are well mixed up and covered with water. Leave them to steep for twenty-four hours. At the end of that time, pour everything into a kettle and boil it up two or three times. Strain off the broth and compress the roses as hard as you can in a press or between two pieces of wood until nothing remains except dry white roses. The broth will look like red wine and will smell like rose-water. Pour everything into a Venetian glass container suitable for the purpose. Next take a further 500 stripped roses and, as before, put them into the pitcher. Then take the said broth and heat it until it is almost boiling. At that stage pour it over the roses and, if there is not enough, add a little boiling water. Leave the mixture to steep again for a further twenty-four hours. At the end of that time